"A Sitlith on Xecho! I would have sworn that was impossible."

"Nothing is impossible," Tau said. He was right, as all spacemen knew. What would be wildly impossible, improbable, not to be believed on one world, might prove commonplace on another planet. Wild nightmares on Terra were upright and worthy citizens on alien soil. Customs so bizarre as to be unbelievable became ritual by law elsewhere. So, long ago spacemen who hunted the lesser known and newly opened planets, had come to believe anything, no matter how incredible it might seem to the planet-bound.

"We have a dead man, a mask," Wilcox summarized, "an alien supposed to be planet-bound but appearing parsecs from its native world, a box that has vanished, and a cargo master back from the dead—and no solution so far. Unless we can find a hint or two before we planet—"

"We have something else." Frank Mura appeared in the doorway. "We have two missing brachs."

POSTMARKED THE STARS is one of Andre Norton's most suspenseful science-fiction novels . . . and it marks the return of Dane Thorson and the *Solar Queen.*

ANDRE NORTON

Postmarked the Stars

ACE BOOKS

A Division of Charter Communications Inc.
1120 Avenue of the Americas
New York, N. Y. 10036

1. RUDE AWAKENING

He was crawling on hands and knees through a world of steam, of greasy mud that sought to engulf him bodily. He could not breathe—yet he must go—get away—out—

His lanky body was sprawled across the bed, arms wide and spread. Hands clawed feebly at the wrinkled covering bunched under it as his head turned with slow, agonized steadiness back and forth on the slightly raised section at one end of that narrow shelf.

Humid heat, gluey mess holding him—but he must keep going. It was very necessary—he must!

He was breathing in gasps, which grew into shudders, shaking his whole lean length. And though his eyes were still closed, he endeavored to push himself up and away from the surface on which he lay.

He could see—his eyes relayed a message to his brain—that he was not crawling over any steam-pillared swamp. Instead, he lifted his head higher to look at walls that appeared to raise and lower rhythmically to his gasping.

Dane Thorson, assistant cargo master, the free trader *Solar Queen*, Terra registry 65-724910-JK—as if they were part of a flaming scarlet sign printed on the heaving surface before him, he read those words. And they made sense, although—did he see them? He—he was Dane Thorson. And the *Solar Queen*—

With a gasp that was half cry, he gave himself a push so he was seated, not lying, on the bed, though he had to hold on tightly while the surface, which should have offered solid security, bucked and swung under him.

But as if recognition of his identity unlocked some barrier, he could think. He was still deathly ill and dizzy, but he could force himself to sort out the events of the immediate past, or at least part of it. He was Dane Thorson, acting cargo master of the *Queen* because Van Ryke, his superior, was off-world and would join them only at the end of this voyage. And this was the *Solar Queen*, a free trader—

But as Dane turned his head carefully, he knew that that was not true. He was not in his familiar cabin on board ship—this was a room. He forced himself to study his surroundings for some clue to aid limping memory. There was the bed on which he had been lying, two snap-down seats pulled out of the wall, no windows but an air plate near the ceiling, two doors, both closed. A wan light came from a ceiling set rod. It was a bare room, not unlike a cell. A cell—memory spiraled back.

They had been Patrol posted. This was a cell— No! That was all done with. They had finned down on Xecho, ready to ship out for Trewsworld on their first mail run—

Ship out! As if those two words were a spur, Dane tried to get to his feet. He nearly fell, but somehow he balanced along the wall, his stomach heaving for tortured moments of misery. He caught at the nearest door, his weight dragging it open, and found that some merciful instinct had brought him to the fresher. Then he proceeded to be thoroughly and violently ill.

Still shaking from racking spasms, he managed to get to water and splash it over his face and upper body, thus becoming aware for the first time that he was not wearing his uniform tunic, though breeches and space boots still clothed him.

The water and, oddly, the nausea, seemed to pull him farther out of the fog. He wavered back into the room, staring about him while he thought. His last clear memory was —what?

Message—what message? That there was a registered package to be picked up, under standard one priority. For a few seconds he had a clear mental picture of the cargo master's office on the *Queen*, of Tang Ya, the com-tech, standing in the door.

Last-minute pickup—last minute! The *Queen* was set for takeoff!

Panic hit him. He did not know what had happened. The message—and he must have left the ship—but where was *here*? And—even more important—when was *now*? The *Queen* had a schedule all the more important because she

6

was, if temporarily, a mail ship. How long had he been here? Surely they would not have lifted without him! And how and why, as well as where—

Dane rubbed a hand across his sweating forehead. Odd, he was dripping with sweat, and yet he shook with a chill inside. There was a tunic— He wavered to the bed and fumbled with the garment that had been tossed there.

Not his. It was not the sober brown of a spaceman but rather a gaudy, though faded, purple with raveling embroidery. But because he was so cold, he pulled it about him. Then he made for the other door, one that must get him out of here—wherever *here* was! The *Queen* set to lift and he not on board—

His legs still tended to buckle under him, but he kept on them and walking. The door gave to his weak shove, and he was in a corridor, with a long line of other doors, all closed. But at the far end was an arch and beyond that movement and sound. Dane headed for that, still trying to remember more. The message for a pickup— He must have left the *Queen* at once. Now he halted to look down at his body under the flapping of the unfastened tunic, too tight and short for him. His safe belt—yes, he was still wearing that. But—

With one hand he investigated. Its pockets were all empty except the one holding his ident disk, but no one would have any use for that. It was keyed to his body chemistry. Let another take it, and within minutes the information on it would be erased. So he had been robbed.

But why the room? If he had been jumped, they would have left him lying— Gingerly he felt his head—no painful bruise or lump. Of course there were nerve holds that knocked a man out, and if sleep gas had been blown in his face— But why the room?

Time for puzzles later. The *Queen* and takeoff—he had to reach the *Queen!* And where was he? How much time did he have? But surely when he had not returned, they would not have gone. Rather they would have come looking for him. The crew of the *Solar Queen* was too close-knit a companionship to leave one of their members planet-side without a search.

At least he could move better now, and his head was clear. Dane pulled the tunic close about him, though he could not seal it, as he reached the arch and looked beyond. The large room was familiar. Half of it had booths set along the wall with dials for quick meals in their tables. The other half had a registration robo, a message bank, and a newscast screen. This was the—the—

He could not remember the name, but it was one of the small, cheap inns at the port, catering mainly to crewmen who were waiting to ship out. He had eaten at that table right over there with Rip Shannon and Ali Kamil just yesterday— or was it yesterday?

The *Queen* and lift time— Panic-fed urgency clamped on him again. At least he was not miles from the port, though on this world where dry land was merely strings of islands set in shallow, steaming seas, one could not get miles from the port and still be on the same blob of land.

All that was of no consequence now. He must get back to the *Queen.* To hold to that was going to take all his concentration. Dane took one careful step after another, heading for the nearest door.

Had he or had he not seen one of those men seated in the nearest booth start up as if he wanted to stop him? Maybe he looked as if he needed assistance. But just let him get to the *Queen—!*

If he attracted any more attention, Dane neither knew nor cared. What filled his world was the supreme luck of seeing an unoccupied scooter just outside. He fumbled his ident disk out, and as he fell rather than sat on the seat, he fed that into the proper slot and punched out "go."

Already he was straining to see the launch strip. One, two, three ships! And the last one in line was the *Queen!* He would make it. The scooter whirled him at its top speed, though he did not remember punching it. It was almost as if the machine sensed his fear and impatience.

The cargo hatch was closed, but, of course, he had seen to that himself. The ramp was still out. As the scooter swept up, he tottered from it to the ramp and pulled himself up hand over hand by the guardrail. His will kept him going, but the weakness and dizziness were returning. And now, the ramp was moving! They were preparing for takeoff!

Dane made a convulsive effort, gained the end of the ramp and then the hatch. He could not reach his own cabin in time to strap down. Where? Van Ryke's was the nearest—up ladder.

His own body was the enemy he must fight. Dane was dimly aware of the struggle with the ladder, of half falling through a cabin door, of reaching the bunk and dropping on it. Then he blacked out.

No dream now of wading through an adhesive swamp or veils of steam. There was a heavy pressure on his chest, smothering him, a harsh rasping on his chin. Dane opened his eyes to stare into inquisitive feline ones. Sinbad, ship's cat, nosed him again, kneaded his paws on Dane under his own portly frame with vigor enough to bring a protest out of the man.

There was the familiar vibration, though. This was Sinbad. He had reached the *Queen*, and they were out in space. A vast relief flooded through Dane.

Then, for the first time he was able to think farther than just reaching the ship before it lifted. He had gone to make a registered pickup. And somewhere he had been jumped and robbed. Before or after he had made the pickup? A new worry presented itself. If he had signed for it, then he, or rather the *Queen*, was responsible for the loss. The sooner he reported to Captain Jellico, the better.

"Yes," he said aloud, pushing Sinbad away to sit up. "Got to see the Old Man—"

His first awakening in the inn had been tough. This was almost as bad. He had to hold onto the bunk and close his eyes, not sure if he *could* move. There was the com on the wall. Get to that, call for help— Poison? Could they—the mysterious they—or he—or it—who had initiated his attack have used poison on him? Once before he had been so wracked, on Sargol, when, by native custom as a successful gorp hunter, he had shared a ceremonial drink—to pay for that compliance later. Tau—Medic Tau—

Dane set his teeth, grasped Van Ryke's file of micro films, which jutted conveniently from the wall, and pulled himself up. He managed to jerk the mike from its hook, but when it came to thumbing the button for sick bay, he could not be sure—they were a blur. He had to chance it.

Now that he was up, he was almost afraid to return to the bunk. The waves of sickness seemed less overpowering when he was on his feet. Maybe if he tried now to get around— Besides, he had to report to Jellico, must do that—

He heard a warning growl from Sinbad as his foot touched something soft. And the big cat, his dignity injured by interference with his tail, slapped back, his claws grating on Dane's space boot.

"Sorry." Dane, trying to avoid the rest of Sinbad's bulk, staggered forward, out of the door, into the well of the ladder. He held out groping hands for that. Captain—must report—

"What the—?"

Dane had not trodden on the head of the man climbing up, but it was a near thing. As with Sinbad, he tried to avoid collision and swung out so far he would have fallen had not the newcomer caught him. Ali Kamil's finely featured face swung back and forth in Dane's sight, but then the assistant engineer's tough grip steadied him.

"Got—to—report," Dane said. "See—Captain—"

"What by the Five Names of Stayfoll" Kamil supported him back against the wall. His face was clear and then blurred in Dane's sight.

"See Jellico—" Dane repeated. He knew he was saying that, but he could not hear his own voice. Nor could he twist free from Kamil's grip.

"Down—come on—"

Not down—up! He had to go to see Jellico—

He was on the ladder. He must have made Ali understand. Only, they were going down—down—up—in space which was which? Dane shook his head to clear it, and that only made it worse, so that he dared not move at all, but clung to the ladder, a sole anchor in a spinning world.

Hands pulled at him. He heard talking, only the words had no meaning.

"Report—" With a vast effort he got that out in a rasping whisper.

There were two of them with him, Ali and someone else. Dane dared not turn his head to see. And they were steering him to a cabin door. Ali pushed that back, and they entered, Dane limp between them.

Then for a stark moment the mists were gone, wiped away. He hung between the two who had supported him, but he could see, as if the shock of what lay on the bunk had pulled him out of the dizzy spin of the sickness.

The sleeper lay quietly, acceleration straps still about him as if he had not recovered from takeoff. His tunic—his head —the face—

Dane gave a jerk that 'loosened the grasp of those with him. Their astonishment must have been as great as his. He stumbled forward the step or two to the bunk to stare down at the man who lay there, eyes closed, apparently asleep or unconscious. Then, holding on with one hand to keep his precarious balance, Dane reached out the other to assure himself by touch that someone *did* lie there, that his eyes were not playing tricks on him, for the face against the raised end of the bunk was the one he saw in mirrors. He was looking down at—*himself!*

There was solid flesh and bone meeting the prod of his finger. But if a body did lie there, the face—was that a dream out of his illness? Dane turned his head. Kamil was there, and with him Frank Mura, the cook steward. Both of them were staring at the man on the bunk.

"No!" Dane choked out a denial of what he saw. "I'm— I'm—*me!* I'm Dane Thorson." And he recited the same formula that had come to him in the inn on his first waking into the nightmare.

"Dane Thorson, assistant cargo master, the free trader *Solar Queen*, Terra registry 65-724910-JK." His ident disk! He had that as proof. Now he got it out of his belt pocket, held it so they might see it, too, and know that he was Dane Thorson. But if he was Dane Thorson, then who—

"What is going on?"

Tau! Medic Tau! With relief Dane hunched around, still keeping his hold on the bunk lest he sprawl on the floor. Tau would know who he was. Why, he and Craig Tau had gone through almost as bad as this together—on Khatka.

"I'm Dane," he said. "I can prove it. You're Craig Tau, and we were on Khatka, where you used magic to make Limbuloo hunt himself. And—and"—he pointed with the ident disk to Ali, his hand shaking as he did it—"you're Ali Kamil, and we found you trapped in a maze on Limbo. And you, you're Frank Mura. You piped us into that maze." There, he must have proved it. No one but Dane Thorson would know all that. They must believe him now.

But then who—what—lay on his bunk, wearing his tunic

11

—because it was his. There was the mend he had done by thoro-weave three days ago. He was Dane Thorson—

"I *am* Dane Thorson—" Not only were his hands shaking now; his whole body quivered. And he was going to be sick again. He couldn't help it. Maybe—maybe this was all some kind of crazy dream!

"Steady! Get him, Kamil." Tau was with him. Then he was in the fresher once more, vomiting.

"Can you hold him?" He heard Tau's voice faintly as if it came from a distance. "I'll have to get a shot. He's been—"

"Poisoned, I think," Dane heard himself say. But whether he spoke aloud, he could not tell. At the same moment the lights went out.

For the third time he roused, but this time lazily. It was not Sinbad's weight on his chest and the cat's rasping tongue that drew him back to consciousness. Rather it was a feeling of peace, as if he had thrown off some burden. And for a long moment he was content until memory began its irritating prick-prick of summons to full awareness.

There was something—something about a report to the captain. Dane's thoughts uncoiled sluggishly. He opened his eyes, turned his head a little, and things dropped into focus. He was in sick bay. Though he had never lain here before, the cabin was familiar. He stirred, and the medic came into Dane's line of vision.

"With us again, eh? Let's see—" He went to work with quick competence to run a check on Dane's still inert body. "Fair enough, though by rights you should be dead."

Dead? He had been dead— Dane frowned. There had been a body in his bunk.

"The man in my bunk?" He made that a question, though he did not finish it.

"Dead. And I think you are fit enough now—" Tau went to the wall com. "Sick bay calling Captain."

Captain—report to the captain! Dane tried to get up, but Tau had already pressed the button bringing part of the surface up under him as a support. A little dizziness returned but then was gone.

"That man—how—"

"Acceleration with a heart condition. He had no business trying to get off-planet," Tau told him.

"His—his face—"

Tau took something from a nearby shelf. He faced Dane, holding out a plasta mask. Save that it had no eyes, only holes, it was like looking in a mirror. And a back stretch covered with blond hair like Dane's turned it into a full head covering.

"Who was he?" The mask possessed a macabre fascination. Dane looked away from it quickly. It was almost like seeing a part of himself limp and flaccid in the medic's grasp.

"We were hoping—are hoping—you know," Tau returned. "But the captain wants it now."

As if that were an introduction, Captain Jellico came in. His deeply tanned face with the blaster scar along one cheek showed no readable emotion, as was usual. But he glanced from the mask Tau was holding to Dane and back again.

"Diabolically clever piece of work," he commented. "Not a quick job."

"Nor made on Xecho either, I would say." Tau put away the mask, to Dane's relief. "That is the product of an expert."

The captain came to Dane's side and held out his hand. On the palm rested a colored tridee. It was of a man. His skin did not have the brown tan of a crewman but was bleached looking, though he must be Terran or Terran colonial bred. There was an odd, fixed look in his eyes, a frozen stillness to his features that was disquieting. His hair was sparse, sandy brown, his eyebrows above those fixed eyes were thin and ragged, and he had a rash of freckles across his upper cheekbones. To Dane he was a complete stranger.

"Who—?"

Jellico gestured to the mask. "The man behind that. You don't know him?"

"Never saw him—that I can remember."

"He had your belongings, a forged ident in the bargain, and that mask. He was sent aboard to be you. And where were you?"

Dane outlined his adventures after waking in the inn, adding the information about the missing package—if it was missing.

"Inform the port police?" he suggested tentatively.

"Not for robbery, I think." Jellico turned the tridee to look down at the face in it, as if, by the very intensity of his gaze, he could force some answer to the riddle. "This was a setup that required a lot of planning. It was, I believe, a means of getting a man on board."

"A cargo master aboard, sir," Dane corrected eagerly, "who would have access to—"

Jellico nodded sharply. "Fair assumption. Stowage reports—what are we shipping that would be worth such a long-range plan?"

Dane, entrusted for the first time with full authority for the stowage, could have recited the entire list. He ran over it swiftly now in his mind. But there was nothing—nothing that important. A mask would require time to make, a reason for a long-thought-out buildup. He turned to Tau.

"I *was* poisoned?"

"You were. If it hadn't been for the metabolism shift after that ceremonial drink on Sargol—" He shook his head. "Whether they meant to have you dead or just put you out for a long time—anyway, normally it would have finished you."

"Then he was meant to be me—for how long?" He asked that question of himself, but the captain answered.

"No longer than Trewsworld, I would say. First, unless he was exceptionally well briefed, he couldn't play the part with shipmates who really knew you. It would require a complete memory switch for that, and they didn't have you in their hands long enough for that. You went off-ship and apparently were back again in one Xechoian cin-cycle. A memory switch takes a planetary day at least. Also, he couldn't play sick either. Tau would have been after him. So, he could say he was uncertain about his work—first run for him in cargo command—and could hold up to check his tapes and the like. The Trewsworld run is not a long one. He might have been able—with luck—to pull it off, or think he could, with that excuse.

"Second, there are only two reasons why he'd come on board—he was carrying something he had to transport under guard, or he himself had a very necessary reason for reaching Trewsworld in disguise. He was defeated mainly by chance—first, that you had your insides shaken up badly on Sargol so that their poison didn't work, and, second, that he himself was not fit for space travel."

"Did he bring anything with him?" Dane asked. "The registered package—they might have been after that all the time but have planned to walk off with it on Trewsworld, not jump me for it on Xecho."

"Trouble was," Jellico answered, "he was checked on board by the ramp cell, not by any of us. We don't know whether he brought anything or not. There's nothing in the cabin, and the holds are safe-locked."

Safe-locked!

"Not the treasure room," Dane returned. "I left that on half seal—couldn't close it until the package came."

Jellico went to the com. "Shannon!" His call to the bridge alerting the assistant astrogator was loud enough to make Dane's ears ring. "Down to the treasure room on the double. See if it's fully sealed or not!"

Dane tried to think. Where else, if the holds were on full seal, where else could something be hidden on the *Queen?*

2. MEMORY LOST AND FOUND

"Two holds full seal, treasure half seal." Rip's voice rang hollowly over the inter-cabin com, loud enough for Dane to hear. Captain Jellico looked to him for confirmation, and he nodded.

"As I left them. Must check the treasure—" Once on full seal, the intruder could not have opened either of the lower compartments where the bulk of their cargo rested. But the treasure room, for registered and special security shipments— Since nothing had been found in Dane's cabin with the dead stranger and it was apparent from the fact he had strapped down that he had intended to ride out the voyage and not use the elaborate disguise for an on-and-off invasion of the *Queen,* then if he did bring something on board, they had better find out what as quickly as possible.

"You're in no shape—" began Tau, but Dane was already sitting up.

"*We* may be in no shape later if I don't!" he returned grimly. Once before the *Queen* had carried an almost lethal cargo unwittingly, and that memory would ride with her crew for years. Wood taken on ship on Sargol had been infested with creatures able to assume the color of anything they touched, creatures whose claws carried a soporific that hit the crew like a plague.

Dane was sure an inspection of the treasure room would assure him whether or not there was any unaccounted-for cargo on board, since a cargo master by long training carried most of his inventory in his head, as well as on record tapes.

They had to let him do it. The safety of the *Queen* by necessity came above all else. But it was Tau who gave him a shoulder to lean on and the captain himself who went down ladder ahead of Dane, reaching up to support the younger man's weak legs.

And Dane needed that support by the time they reached the level of the treasure room. He held fast to Tau for a long instant, his heart pounding, gasping. Now Tau's words that he had been very close to death struck starkly, but he stumbled on, reaching for the release.

Trewsworld was a frontier planet, lightly settled. The bulk of the mail they carried for her single port city was light—micro tapes of agricultural information, personal communications between settlers and off-world, a bag of official tapes for the Patrol post. There was little enough security material, and the major portion was the embryo boxes.

Since the importation of domestic animals was experimental on most worlds and very carefully supervised, any such shipment was top security. And Ecology had firm rules on what might or might not be transferred. Too many times in the past, the balance of nature on some planet had been thoughtlessly overturned by such importation of a life form that had no local enemy, which perhaps developed a mutated strain beyond control, to speedily become a menace rather than the source of profit the importers had intended.

After exhaustive tests the pioneers were allowed imports of embryos for stock raising, and the *Queen* now carried fifty such—lathsmer chicks in sealed containers. These were lab-developed and worth far more than their weight in credits—since Trewsworld had proved an acceptable climate and lathsmer fowl were luxury items across a wide sector of

16

space. Not only could the adults be plucked once a year for their fine down, but young chicks were epicures' delight for the table. If the lathsmer were raised in quantity, the pioneer settlers of the planet had an export item to establish them firmly in galactic trade.

To Dane these were the major "treasures" the *Queen* carried. But the boxes were secured by double bolting and shock packing, just as he had supervised. They were intact and protected. The few other bags and boxes were as undisturbed, and he finally had to admit that as far as he could tell, there had been no tampering. But when Tau helped him out, he double-sealed the portal as it should have been before the *Queen* lifted.

The original problem remained unsolved. A dead man in a mask, aboard for what reason? Until they came out of hyper, which meant into the Trewsworld system, there was no chance to communicate with the Patrol or other authorities.

Tau had made a detailed study of the body before it had been sealed off in a hull pocket for deep freeze. Save that the stranger had plainly died from a heart condition aggravated by the strain of take-off, that examination told them nothing. The man was of Terran descent with no mutating modifications. In these years of space travel he could have been any age past youth and from a number of worlds where the inhabitants were so akin to Terrans as to make them indistinguishable. None of the *Queen*'s crew had seen him before, nor was the poison used on Dane isolated and named by the medic, in spite of his research.

The forgery of the ident disk was perfect. Jellico stood now flipping that back and forth as if it alone could somehow prove a key to unlock the puzzle.

"Such a careful plan means a big deal. You say that call to pick up the security package came through the field tower?" he asked Dane.

"Regular channels. I had no reason to doubt it."

"Probably was straight, as far as they knew. Anyone could have put it in to them," Steen Wilcox, the astrogator, commented. "You're sure there's nothing on the manifests that is suspicious?"

"Nothing." Dane suppressed a sigh. Of course he was only a stand-in for Van Ryke (and how he wished now that the

17

usually omniscient cargo master was here and that he himself could return to the less responsible role of assistant), but at least he *knew* what he had seen stored away. He had personally clamped most of it into the special racks. The biggest things they had handled were the embryo boxes and the brach cage. The brach cage! That was the only thing he had not remembered, mainly because its inhabitants, being alive and needing attention, had been placed in Mura's territory off the hydrop compartment.

"What about the brachs?" he asked now.

Tau had a ready answer. "Nothing there. I give them daily inspection. The female's about to have kits—not until after we planet—but she should be checked. That traveling cage can't conceal anything."

Dane thought about the brachs. They were common on Xecho—the largest native animal, that is, land animal.

But that did not make them very big. An adult male was about as tall as Dane's knee, the female slightly larger. They were amusing, appealing creatures, covered with a soft growth that was really neither fur nor under-feathers but had some of the texture of both. This was cream-colored with a faint rosy underlight in the female, darker in the male, who was in addition equipped with folds of skin under his throat that could be inflated and, when so, flushed crimson. Their heads were long with pointed, narrow muzzles and a small, sharp horn on the very tip, which they put to excellent use when dealing with their favorite food, a shell-fish that had to be pried open. The ears had feathery fringe. They were easily tamed but now rigidly protected by law on Xecho after early settlers there had carried on an illegal trade in their skins. Selected pairs were sometimes exported only under bond to specialists in xenobiology, as these were due to be delivered to a lab on Trewsworld. For some reason they seemed to present a puzzle to most biologists, and several different planets had scientists devoting time to a detailed study of them.

"That's it," Dane said a short time later. He had run through the tape of inventory—nothing anywhere, except a dead man who must have been part of a very elaborate plan.

"So—" Wilcox looked as if he were now faced with one of his beloved mathematical formulas, one that was new and he was now admiring, before solving, for its very intricacy.

18

"If this was not for the cargo, it is the man himself. He needed to get to Trewsworld under cover. Either the disguise was meant to operate to pass him at both ports or one alone. He risked our uncovering him and putting him under arrest. And murder, since they must have meant to eliminate you permanently"—he nodded to Dane—"is a very high price to pay. What's going on on Trewsworld according to rumor?"

Planet politics could be a perilous business on some worlds, as they all knew. Free traders carefully did not take sides. It was hammered into every crewman that the ship itself was his planet and to it he owed allegiance, first, last, and always. No involvement in local matters. That could be a hard fact to face when one's sympathies or emotions were aroused by sights and sounds, but every one of them knew that it was the backbone of their own lives and it must be adhered to. So far, Dane had never come face to face with a choice between the ship's safety and his own emotional urge to join or refrain. He knew that he had been lucky, and he only hoped that luck would continue to hold for him. He did not know whether any of the others had faced that dilemma, but the past, before he had joined the Queen, was theirs and not his to remember.

"Nothing off course that I know of." Jellico still slapped the ident disk against the palm of his hand. "We'd have been warned in the general orders if there was. Combine had this run. They turned over all their general tapes with the contract."

"There is always," Ali said, "the I-S."

I-S—Inter-Solar. Twice in the past the Solar Queen had had a brush with that company. And both times the free trader had won the round, a pygmy successfully facing down one of the giants of the star lanes. The companies with their huge trading empires, their fleets of ships, thousands, even millions of employees strung out along the galactic trade routes, were monopolists, sparring with each other for the control of new planet trade. The free traders were the beggars at the feast, snatching at such crumbs of profit as the big ones overlooked contemptuously, or thought it not worth the effort to exploit.

The Solar Queen had held a contract on Sargol for the taking of Koros gems—her captain had even fought a Salarik duel with an I-S man to claim and hold their rights. It was the I-S who had had the *Queen* proclaimed a plague ship when the mysterious pest they had unwittingly brought aboard with cargo had knocked out most of the crew. And only grit, determination, and an appeal made over the law, but effectively, to Terra at large, broadcast from a port by the junior members, who had not succumbed to the pest, had saved their ship and their lives.

And it had again been an I-S representative whose poaching trade they had broken on Khatka when Captain Jellico, Medic Tau, and Dane had visited there at the Chief Ranger's request during what might have been a disastrous planet leave.

So the I-S people certainly had no love for the *Queen*, and her crew would be inclined to think first of their meddling in any trouble. Dane drew a deep breath. This *could* be I-S! They would have the means, the facilities to set up such a plan. There had not been any I-S ship planeting on Xecho while the *Queen* was there—it was Combine territory—but that meant nothing. They could have shipped in their man on a neutral shuttle from another system. But if this was part of an I-S plot—

"Could be," Jellico returned. "But I doubt it. In the first place, they may not look upon us with any warmth of feeling —or at least a warmth of feeling we would relish. But to them we are very small fry. If they saw a chance to fuse our tubes without difficulty, they'd probably do it. But to set up some elaborate plan—no. We're carrying mail, and any trouble would bring a Patrol investigation. I won't cut out I-S, but they are not my first choice. Combine reported no political trouble on Trewsworld, so what—"

"There is one way of learning something." Tau drummed absently on the edge of a swing shelf with his fingertip, and Dane caught himself watching that. Craig Tau's hobby was magic, or rather those unexplainable powers and talents that the primitive (and sometimes not so primitive) men on half a thousand worlds used to gain their ends. He had used his knowledge of such things to bring them safely out of danger on Khatka, and in that particular action a drum had had a great deal to do with the building up of whatever force he *had* drawn upon to break the will of a feared witch doctor. Only Dane had beat the drum then, to Tau's orders.

Now it was almost as if some suggestion reached from the medic's mind to his. Though Dane had no claim to esper talents, Tau had admitted that was in fact why he had made a good foil on Khatka.

"You can't remember what happened between your leaving the ship and your awaking in the inn, consciously," the medic continued. Dane lost interest in that drumming finger and guessed.

"Deep probe?"

"Will it work?" Jellico demaded.

"You can't tell until you try. Dane has a block against some hypo techniques. How deep that goes, we can't tell. But the dead man was wearing his tunic, which means they might have met. If he's willing to try, deep probe might give us some answers."

Dane wanted to shout "no" with all the force the illness had left in him. Deep probe was used on criminals by court order. If a man were susceptible enough, it would wring every incident of his life out of him back to the first childhood memories. But they would not be after that, just the immediate past. Dane could see the sense in Tau's suggestion. It was just that to accept it meant facing up to something from which he shrank with every fiber of his being.

"We can set it only for the time you left the ship." Tau appeared to understand the cause of his reservation. "And it may not work—you're not a good subject—plus the fact we have no idea what alteration of body chemistry the poison may have worked. In one way, such a testing might be to your advantage, for then we can judge any change that dose may have caused."

Dane felt a return of that same chill that had struck him when he had fought for strength in the inn. Did Tau believe that he had taken mental damage? But he had remembered the stowage, and the tapes had confirmed the accuracy of his memory. There was only the period of time that Tau wanted to research that eluded him. He wavered—the distaste for the probe's revelations, together with a feeling he did *not* want to know if the drug had affected him, combined to make him hesitate. Only, if he did not agree, then in days to come his ignorance might be worse to face than certain knowledge.

"All right," he said, and then, for a second or two, wished he had refused.

Since the ship was in hyper and needed only a standby watch on the bridge, Rip was set that duty, and both the captain and Wilcox were present as Tau made ready to activate a probe. Dane was not quite certain how it worked, though that it was able to turn a man inside out as far as his past was concerned was a known fact.

Jellico made ready to tape what Dane would report, and Tau gave him the shot to send him under. He heard a dwindling murmur and then—

He was going down the ramp, a little worried and resentful of this last-minute call to pick up a security package. Luckily there was a field scooter parked not too far away. He scrambled in, fed in his ident disk, and gave it the order for the gate.

"The Deneb." He repeated aloud his destination, having a vague idea it was an eating place not too far from the field. At least that much was in his favor. And he had the receipt tape to hand, needing only the voice and thumb record of the shipper to make it legal.

The scooter delivered him at the gate, and he looked down the offport street for some sign of the café he wanted. Xecho was a crosslane planet, a port of call for ships switching from one sector to another. Thus it did have an off-port section of inns, eating places, and amusement holes for space crews, but it was relatively small and tame compared to such sections ringing the ports of other worlds, consisting of a single street of closely packed one-story buildings.

As usual, the heat of late afternoon was intense. Dane was wearing full uniform tunic and breeches, which added to his discomfort. He must make this excursion as short as possible. He searched for any identifying sign of the establishment he wanted. Those bright lights that would be visible at night were missing now, and it took him several moments of survey to find it—a small place sandwiched in between a hock-lock and an inn he remembered having eaten in the day before.

There were not many on the street—the heat kept most planetside dwellers inside. He passed only two crewmen as he made the best speed the sultry day heat would allow to his goal, and he did not look closely at either.

To step inside the Deneb was to step from a furnace into cool dusk and relief against the punishment of Xecho's day. It was not a restaurant, rather a drinking place, and he was uneasy. For someone with a packge needing security insurance, to be waiting here was not normal—but then this was his first mail run, and how could he gauge what was normal procedure. If he got voice and thumb records, then the *Queen* was only responsible for the safe transportation of the article in question, and if he had continued doubts, he need only step into the security office at the port on his way back and make an additional recording for the complete coverage of the *Queen*'s part in an affair that might be on the shady side.

There was a line of booths against the far wall with dials for drinks and various legal smokes. But knowing off-ports, Dane wondered if some illegal stimulants could not also be ordered if one knew the proper code. The place was very quiet. A crewman was in a drunken doze in the farthest booth, an empty glass before him, his fingers still curled protectingly about it.

There was no sign of any proprietor, and the small booth beside the door was empty. Dane waited impatiently for a moment or two. Surely the drunk in the corner had not sent for him. At last he rapped on the surface of the pay-booth grill, the noise carrying more loudly through the room than he expected.

"Softly, softly—"

The words were Basic but delivered with a hissing intonation that slurred them into what was just a series of "s" sounds. The curtain at the back of the booth had been pulled aside, and a woman came in—that is, she was almost humanoid enough to be termed that, though her pallid skin was covered with minute scales, and the growth that hung about her shoulders was not strictly hair, fine-fringed though it was. Her features were enough like his own not to be remarkable. She was wearing an affectation of Terran sophistication that he had last seen on that planet, narrow trousers of metallic cloth, a sleeveless jerkin of puff fur, and a half mask of silver-copper that covered eyes and forehead and hung part way over the nose in whorls of metal.

The dress, high-style Terran, was as out of place in this

dingy hole as a drink of Lithean champagne would be, although it served as a disguise.

"You wish—?" Again that hissing speech.

"A call was made to the mail ship, Gentle Fem, the *Solar Queen*, asking that a security package be picked up for shipment."

"Your ident, Gentle Homo?"

Dane held it out, and she bent her head a little as if the elaborate mask made it as hard for her to see as it was for others to view her face.

"Ah. Yes, there is such a package."

"You are the sender?"

"Please to come this way." She evaded his question, opened the front of the booth as if it were a door, and beckoned Dane beyond, looping the curtain for him to pass through.

There was a very narrow corridor, so narrow a vent that his shoulders brushed the wall on either side. Then a second door, one set in the wall, rolled aside as he approached it, probably set on an entra beam.

The room into which he went was in contrast to the dinginess of the Deneb's open serving section. It was paneled in plasta sheets, which melted into one another in a never-ending view of wide sweeps of alien landscapes. In spite of the beauty of the walls, however, there was an assault on Dane's nostrils that almost made him gag. He could see no source of that terrible stench—it just was, though the furnishings of the room were luxurious and its general aspect one of taste with plenty of credits to gratify it.

A man sprawled in an easi-rest. He did not rise as Dane came in nor greet him with more than a stare. The woman paid no attention to him but swiftly went past Dane to the other side of the room and picked up a box of dull metal, a square cube as large as two palms' width.

"This you take," she said.

"Who signs?" Dane looked from her to the man, who still stared at him so steadily that the Terran felt uncomfortable.

The man said nothing at all, though there was a small period of silence as if the woman waited for some order or move from him. Then she spoke.

"If it is needful, then so will I do."

"It is necessary." Dane brought out his recorder and leveled the lens at the box.

"What you do?" the woman cried out with urgency as if he proposed to shoot the package out of her hand.

"Take an official recording," he told her. She had the box pressed tightly between both hands, the fingers outstretched so that she appeared to be trying to cover as much of its surface with her own flesh and bone as she could.

"You ship that," Dane continued, "and you must go by the rules."

Again it was as if she waited for some sign from the man, but he had not moved, nor did his eyes drop from their survey of Dane. Finally, with visible reluctance, she put the box on the edge of a small table and stepped back, though she hovered close by, her hands even outstretched, as if ready to snatch it to safety if threatened.

Dane pressed the button, took a picture of the shipment, then held out the mike of the voice tape.

"Verify that you are shipping this by security, Gentle Fem. Give your name, the date, and then press your thumb on the tape roll—right here."

"Very well. If this is the regulation, then I must do." But she picked up the box and held it against her as she leaned forward to take the mike.

Only she did not complete that gesture. Instead, the hand reaching for the mike slashed down at Dane's wrist, and a nail, abnormally long, scored his flesh. For a moment he was too stunned to move. Then his hand and his arm went numb. As it dropped to hang uselessly at his side, the tape fell on the floor. He had strength enough to turn to the door, but he did not get even one step toward safety. His last clear memory was of falling forward to his knees, his head turned a little so that the unwinking stare of the man in the easi-rest was still on him. The other did not move.

There was nothing more until he crawled over a steamy landscape over greasy mud and awakened again sick in the inn room to make his way back to the *Queen.*

Then he awoke, to face the party crowding into sick bay, Tau bending over him with a restorative prick of needle, bringing him fully aware of where he was, but this time able to remember all the probe had brought to the surface of his mind.

3. CARGO TROUBLE

"The tape record." Dane spoke his first thought aloud.

"The only one of your possessions that stranger did not bring with him," Jellico replied.

"And the box?"

"Not here. It might only have been bait."

Somehow Dane did not believe that. The woman's actions, as he remembered them, argued otherwise. Or had they been meant to center his attention wholly on the shipment so he would be unprepared for her attack?

He knew that those crowded into the small sick bay had heard every detail of what he had relived. The probe not only broadcast but also taped it for the record while he was under, so all the few facts were plain.

"How did I get from the Deneb to the inn?" he wondered. There was something else, a small teasing memory of a face so fleetingly seen that he could not be sure. Had or had he not sighted in the outer room of the inn as he staggered out the man who had sat so silently when he had been struck down? He could not be sure.

"They could have carried you in as a drunk," Ali remarked. "Would be common enough in off-port. And I take it you did not stop to make inquiries when you left."

"Had to get back to the ship," Dane returned. He was thinking of the box that had seemed so important to the woman. It had not been large, small enough, in fact, to hide. But they had searched the treasure room, his cabin—

"The box—"

Captain Jellico stood up. "About so big, wasn't it?" He sketched dimensions in the air.

Dane agreed.

"All right. We'll hunt it."

Though he longed to join in that search, Dane was now

tied to the bunk by his own weakness. The secondary shot
Tau had given him was wearing off. He was suddenly so
sleepy that he could not fight the drowsiness. But he knew
that any search the captain organized would be down to the
very plates that made up the *Queen*.

And the search, thorough though it was, revealed nothing,
as Dane discovered when he roused, feeling much more himself than he had since leaving the Deneb. They had a dead
man in deep freeze and nothing else, save the probe tape,
which Captain Jellico played over again until Dane loathed
hearing it, always hoping for some small new detail. There
was only one thing to add to that account, the chance that
the man in the inn who had witnessed his leaving had been
also in the Deneb.

"If that was true, he must have had a shock," the captain
mused. "But it was too late for him to change their plans
then. And we can't do any more until we get to the local
Patrol post on Trewsworld. I'll take word-oath that there is
no box hidden where we looked."

"That woman," the com-tech, Tang Ya, said between sips
of Terran coffee in the mess cabin where Dane had gone on
his first excursion out of sick bay, "she was alien. I've been
wondering—" From the inner pocket of his tunic, he pulled
a sketch block. In sharp, set lines on it a figure was boldly
presented. He put it before Dane. "Look like her?"

Dane was startled. As with all the crew, Tang Ya had his
hobby to relieve the tedium of long voyages. But to Dane's
knowledge, it was the creation of miniature electronic devices,
toys. He had not known the Martian com-tech was also an
artist, or enough of one to produce the picture he now saw.

He studied it critically, not for the skill of the work but
for likeness to face and figure of his memory.

"The face—it was narrower at the chin; the eyes—they
seemed to slant more, unless the mask made them just seem
so."

Ya took up the block, pressed a small indentation on its
rim, and the lines Dane thought set altered into the shape
he had suggested.

"Yes!" But he was still amazed at the alteration.

The com-tech again laid the block on the table, sliding it
along to Captain Jellico, who studied it for a long moment
before he in turn passed it to Tau, and from the medic it

went to Steen Wilcox. The astrogator picked it up and held it closer to the light.

"Sitllith—"

The word meant nothing to Dane but apparently did to the captain, for he almost snatched the plaque back from his second-in-command to give it a second intent examination.

"You're sure?"

"Sitllith!" Wilcox was certain. "But it doesn't fit."

"No," Jellico agreed angrily.

"Just what is Sitllith—or who?" Tau asked.

"What and who both," replied Wilcox. "Alien-humanoid, but really alien to the tenth—"

Dane started, leaning forward to view the picture where it lay before the captain. Alien to the tenth! Xenobiology was a required study for cargo masters, as it was on them that first contact for trade with alien races often rested. Their study of alien customs, desires, and personality factors never ended, but he had never believed that so humanoid a form could contain so alien a personality as Wilcox had stated. It was rather like saying that a Terran snake's identity went about clad in flesh and bones such as his own.

"But she—she talked rationally. She—she was very humanoid—" he protested.

"She also poisoned you," the astrogator replied dryly. "Not with any concoction smeared on her nail either. That was from a gland in her finger! As to how she could appear so close to the human norm, I don't know that. Conditioning might have something to do with it. But a Sitllith on Xechol! They are thought to be planet-bound, to have so great a fear of the open that any attempt to rise from the surface of their world brings about self-death—they frighten themselves to death. Their world is infrared light, so we don't visit them much. I saw just one, in deep freeze back at a lab on Barbarrossa. And it was immature. Its poison sack was empty. It had gone after a Survey scout and stowed away in his ship when he lifted. When it found it was in space"— Wilcox shrugged—"that was the end. He brought it back in deep freeze. But you had an adult, operating off her own world, and I would have sworn that was impossible."

"Nothing is impossible," Tau said. He was right, as all spacemen knew. What would be wildly impossible, improbable, not to be believed on one world, might prove common-place on another planet. Wild nightmares on Terra were upright and worthy citizens (if not by Terran standards) on alien soil. Customs so bizarre as to be unbelievable became ritual by law elsewhere. So, long ago spacemen, and even more free traders, who hunted the lesser known and newly opened planets, had come to believe anything, no matter how incredible it might seem to the planet-bound.

Jellico picked up the sketch again. "This can be fixed to stay?" he asked the astrogator.

"Press in the middle—then the impression will be locked until you wish to release it."

"We have a dead man, a mask"—Wilcox set down his empty mug—"an alien supposed to be planet-bound but appearing parsecs from its or her native world, a box that has vanished, and a cargo master back from the dead—and no solution so far. Unless we can find a hint or two before we planet—"

"We have something else." Frank Mura stood in the door-way. Though he spoke in his usual quiet tone, there was something in his voice that drew their attention. "We have two missing brachs."

"What in the—!" Jellico was on his feet. Because his main interest was that of a xenobiologist, he had spent time ob-serving the animals from Xecho, even taking them to his cabin on occasion for freedom from their cage. Since Queex, the hideous hoobat whose cage hung there, objected so strenuously to their coming that Jellico's usual method of quieting the parrot-crab-toad, that of a smart blow on the floor of its cage to jar it into silence had not sufficed, he had had to transfer Queex elsewhere for the duration of the brachs' visit.

"But the cage lock," he added to his first protest.

Mura extended a hand. Between his fingers was a thin wire, twisted at one end. "This was in that," he stated.

"By the Seven Names of Trutex!" Ali took the bit of wire and held it up, twirling it between thumb and finger. "A pick-lock!"

"It was pulled," Mura continued, "from the netting-inside the cage."

He certainly had all their attention now. Twisted from *inside* the cage? But that must mean—Dane's earlier complacent acceptance of the impossible when it dealt with Sitlliths balked at accepting this particular revelation. Inside the cage meant that the brachs had twisted it free. But the brachs were animals, and not particularly bright animals at that. If he remembered rightly and he should, for that rating was part of the invoices, they did not rank as high on the learning scale as Sinbad, who was now sitting in the far corner of the mess cabin industriously washing his face.

"Let me see that!" Jellico took the wire and studied it with the same concentration he had given to the picture "Broken off—and, yes, it is a pick-lock."

"The brachs," Mura repeated, "are missing."

They could not be in the holds, Dane thought. Those were sealed. That left the engine room, the sick bay, their personal cabins, the control section, and a few other places, none of which could afford much protection for two escaped animals, while the intense search earlier for the box had certainly acquainted the crew with every possible space.

Now they had another hunt. Two animals, perhaps frightened, and with the female pregnant, so that she should not be alarmed, must be handled with more caution. Jellico set up a search party consisting only of those who had had contact with the brachs, since strangers might only send them into some desperate and damaging flight. He called instructions to Stotz in the engine room and ordered the engineer, the two tube men, Kosti and Weekes, together with Ali, who was to return there forthwith, to stay put until their section of the ship was declared empty of brachs.

Wilcox and Ya were to join Shannon on watch duty at the controls, search that section, and seal themselves in and any wandering brach out, leaving the actual search to Dane, Tau, Mura, and the captain, who had petted, fed, and cared for the live cargo. As an added precaution, Sinbad was shut up in the galley.

When the engine room and the control cabin both reported crew in, brachs not present, the other four began. Dane made his way down to the cargo level, but the seals there were intact. There was no way they could have gotten into the holds. The thought of the pick-lock still bothered him. How had the brachs done that? Or had they? Was it only meant to seem that they had freed themselves? But no member of the crew would play such a senseless prank.

And the stranger was dead, in a freeze compartment. Dane's imagination suggested a very macabre explanation, and he found himself turning almost against his will to a side passage, to another compartment door. That, too, was sealed, and he knew with relief that that wild speculation was truly impossible. The dead did not come to life and walk again.

There now remained the personal cabins, those of the engineering staff first. None of them were luxuriously furnished, and their cramped compactness meant that the men who lived in them were forced into meticulous neatness if they were not already that way by habit. There were no lockers, no storage compartments open. He went into each and inspected any possible hiding place, and those of the right size were very few. Each fresher, though the door might be firmly shut, was opened. There was nothing.

Next level up—Van Ryke's combined living quarters and office. Dane stepped inside. Nothing here. Not for the first time since this began, he wished that its usual inhabitant was on board now. They needed Van Ryke. The cargo master's years of experience in all the mazes of trade and alien dealing were, for Dane, the best preparation for solving what had happened now.

The treasure hold across from the cargo master's quarters —seal safely intact, just as he had left it. Next level—junior officers' quarters, Rip's cabin facing his, the hydro garden, the gallery, Mura's section. This was to be the extent of his own exploration, and not all of it, as Mura would cover his quarters and the hydro. Dane had only his cabin and Rip's.

He took Rip's first—all in order—then his own. As he opened the door, only a fraction of off aim saved him. A stun beam clicked along above his ear, sending him reeling back into the corridor. He managed to push shut the slide door and leaned there, holding his spinning head, trying to think coherently. Someone—something—inside was armed with a stunner and had tried to down him when he entered. Had there been another intruder beside the dead man? That was the only possible explanation. He lurched along to the nearest com mike and thumbed the red alert.

"What—?" Wilcox's voice demanded, but it sounded very faint and far away as if the jolt that had brushed Dane had left him partially deaf.

"Someone—my cabin—stunner—" He got out the warning. He was watching the door, though he was not sure how, unarmed, he could prevent that other from leaving if he wanted to.

But if the intruder in Dane's cabin realized he had the advantage, he did not try to use it to force his way out. The Terran tried to think of where any stowaway might have hidden. The interior of the flitter maybe—though to take the acceleration of lift-off, plus the wrench of translation into hyper, without any safeguards would knock most men out. Of course, this might not be a human at all.

There was a clatter on the ladder as Jellico swung down. And Frank Mura came at the same moment from the hydro. Tau followed the captain. The medic went at once to Dane.

"Clipped me with a stunner," he explained.

"Still in there?" Jellico looked to the cabin.

"Yes."

"All right. Tau, how about sleep gas through the air duct?"

The medic pushed Dane closer to the wall with an order of "Stay put!" and then climbed back to his lab on the next level. He returned with a small container and a length of tubing, which he handed over to the captain. "All ready."

"Did you see who it was?" Tau asked as the captain stepped into Rip's cabin and began unscrewing the mesh protector over the air duct.

"No. All happened too fast. After he clipped me, I couldn't see straight, anyway. But where could a stowaway have been—in the flitter?"

"Through lift-off? Well, maybe," Tau conceded, "if he were really tough. But into hyper—I doubt it, unless he took the jump in Shannon's bunk. Shannon was on duty, and the dead man was in yours—"

They could see Jellico through the open door, inserting the tubing, pushing it along with care as he stood on Rip's bunk, his shoulders hunched, concentrating on what he could see of the tube's reptilian passage until it reached the grill of Dane's quarters. Then he made more delicate movements, and Dan guessed he was maneuvering the end of the tube to strike against the grill so that the released gas would go directly into the closed cabin.

"Now!" His grip tightened on the small container in one hand, while with the other he held the mask Tau handed him over his own nose and mouth against any back draft from the tube. The wait for the container to be emptied seemed endless to Dane. He was shaking off the effects of the stunner touch. Finally Jellico pulled back the tube and dropped to the deck.

"If whoever is in there breathes," he said with dour satisfaction, "he's out now."

That statement sounded odd to Dane, almost as if the captain might share that monstrous suspicion about the dead returned to life again.

Dane reached the door first. It was not locked from the inside but gave easily, so they could see in, the masks supplied by Tau now in use by them all, while the medic was using a sucker to draw the fumes out of the air.

Dane so fully expected to see a man that for a second or two he was disconcerted when he sighted nothing of the kind. What lay on the floor of the cabin, one forepaw still resting on the stunner, was the male brach, while curled on the bunk lay the female. And both were unconscious.

"The brachs!" Dane went down on one knee and touched the feathery covering of the male before he believed it true. But it was the brach. There was no one else here. The animal had used the stunner with the intelligence of a man brought to bay. Dane glanced at the captain and for the first time in his service aboard the *Queen* saw Jellico startled out of his usual impassivity.

But Tau had crowded past Dane and was bending over the female brach to make a quick examination.

"She's in labor. Let me through!" He gathered up the limp animal and stepped over the inert male.

"What about it?" Dane looked from the captain to Mura and back to the male brach. "It—it must have used the stunner. But—"

"A trained brach?" suggested the steward. "Conditioned perhaps to use a weapon under certain circumstances?"

"Maybe," Jellico conceded. "But I don't know. Frank, can you make that cage break-proof?"

"Put a chain on, rig an alarm—" Mura listed the possibilities. He came forward to lean over and stare down at the sleeping animal. Dane picked up the stunner and thrust it into the nearest compartment, which he slammed shut.

"An animal," Mura said. "I swear it is—was—an animal.

I have seen brachs. These acted no differently. Why, when I filled their feed bin—" He paused, a slight frown drawing his black brows closer together.

"You filled their feed bin and what happened?" the captain wanted to know.

"This one, the male, watched me latch it. Then he reached through the bars and shook the fastenings. I thought he only wanted more of the renton leaves, and I gave him some. But now I think he was trying the door lock."

"Well, let's get him back in the cage before he wakes up," Jellico said. "And use the chain and the alarm, Mura. We might set a video on and hook it to general screen cast as a precaution. I want a record of what happens when he wakes up."

Mura lifted the brach and carried it back to the cage. Both Jellico and Dane watched him take the precautions that had been suggested. Then Ya was called to rig the video so that they could keep the animal under watch as if he were a suspect in a cell, a snooper on him.

"Who is responsible for this shipment?" Jellico turned to Dane.

"The Norax lab. All the papers are correct. They are to be sent through to the Simplex people on Trewsworld—authorized project by Council permission."

"Nothing about mutants?"

"No, sir. Perfectly ordinary listing. It had all the proper notations, and the Norax people themselves sent a tech with the cage. He set it up and brought in the food and a diet list for Mura."

"He set up the cage," repeated Jellico thoughtfully. The captain raised his hand and set it against the wall above the cage. "Did he pick this particular spot?"

Dane tried to remember. The tech had come on board with two men carrying the cage. Had he picked the place? No, not exactly, and Mura had the answer.

"No, sir. I said here—easier to keep an eye on the animals. But I don't understand. The female—she had a month yet to go. The kits were to be born on Trewsworld."

Captain Jellico slapped the bulkhead behind the cage almost as if he were testing its solid substance.

"Treasure hold below right here," he said. But Dane could see no connection between that and the weird behavior of

34

a pair of brachs—other than that this whole voyage was one mystery after another.

Jellico did not explain. Instead, he hunkered down and asked Mura to explain the details of the fastening. Then Ya came to set up the improvised snooper, which, to Dane's mystification, the captain insisted be concealed from the inhabitant of the cage so that, when the brach awoke, he would not know he was under observation, as if the animal was now a criminal suspect.

All arranged to his satisfaction, Jellico gave a final order to leave the animal alone and for all of them to keep away as much as possible from the cage. Dane, after giving a last look at the peacefully sleeping creature, which, even now, he could hardly believe tried to beam him with his own weapon, went back to his cabin, stretched on his bunk, and tried vainly to make sense of what had happened. He had been through crises before on the *Queen*, but never had there been so inexplicable a series of happenings. Animals that acted with intelligence, a dead man wearing his face, the alien woman—it was as fantastic as a tridee story tape.

Video—what did the captain expect to pick up by the snooper? What of Mura's suggestion that the brach had been conditioned to attack a man? That such a thing was possible was not beyond the bounds of possibility.

Dane rolled off the bunk and went to look up the record of the brach shipment. It was very straightforward, just as he remembered—two brachs, male and female, consigned from the Norax lab on Xecho to the Simplex Ag station on Trewsworld. He had every permit filled out correctly, and unless someone had spent a fortune for forgeries, it was as it should be.

Nevertheless, he pulled out that tape and ran it through for duplication. He had just finished when the com gave an alerting whistle.

"Screen," came Jellico's voice. Dane reached up and triggered the small video screen.

4. TROUBLE FLIGHT

The short corridor and the brach cage flashed into view. The brach was on its feet, its head turning from side to side as if in search of something. Then, showing more intense emotion than Dane would have thought possible for those notoriously amiable creatures, it flung itself at the door of the cage, grasped bar and netting with its paws, and shook them vigorously, as if by that exertion it could tear its way to liberty.

However, its frenzy did not last long. After a moment or two of battering, it squatted back on its haunches, its gaze fixed on the immovable barrier. Its attitude was, Dane thought if he did not know that was impossible, that of an intelligent consideration of the situation, a pause to plan.

It approached the barrier opening again, inserted one paw as far as it could through the open spaces, and explored by touch the new fastening. In those seconds of watching, Dane was converted to the idea he had dismissed so summarily after he had gone over the records a second time. The brach had controlled its first reactions of fear or rage or both and was now exploring the possibility of again mastering the locks that held it prisoner.

Mutant? But if so, the Norax people had defaulted on their permissions, and they were too well established a foundation to try anything of the sort. Also, if these had come from the Norax lab, there was no reason why the techs there should not know they were super-super brains of their species. It left one possible explanation: that, in spite of the records, these were not Norax animals but part of a carefully planned deception, as elaborately set up as the intrusion of the dead stranger. The brach and him—was that the combination they should investigate?

Having run its paws over the fastening and been frustrated

by the lock there, the brach squatted very still, staring straight at the door that cut it off from freedom. Then, as if it had made up its mind, it turned resolutely to the back of the cage and, using the nose horn, pried up a portion of the soft covering over the floor, thick and padded, devised to protect the animals against ship acceleration and hyper jump. It disclosed a place where one of the wires had been rooted up and broken off. Pick-lock—this was where it had gotten the pick-lock!

Dane watched in fascination. Was it going to try the same thing again? Apparently so, for it strained and pushed the nose horn into the already frayed hole, jerking its head up and down to wear away the stubborn wire. It worked steadily, with a concentration and determination Dane had heretofore equated only with his own scale of life.

At last it had broken off a longer section of the wire. Was that by chance, or did it actually understand that the present lock was farther from its reach than the one it had mastered and that it needed more wire to touch it?

Approaching the door again, it poked the wire through, strove to manipulate the new locking bar, and immediately dropped the wire, leaping away with an upward toss of its head as if both alarmed and hurt. Dane knew that it had received a mild shock rigged to prevent just such action.

Again it squatted, drawn in tightly, shaking its paw. Then, holding it tight to its chest, it extended a pale tongue and licked the clawed digits as if to soothe them, though Dane knew that the shock was mild, for a warning, and would not hurt. They had certainly now seen enough to know they were dealing with no ordinary brach.

"Captain!" The com gave out Tau's call. "Sick bay if you please!"

What now? Dane got up. Tau had called for the captain, but if there was some difficulty about the female brach, it was his responsibility, she being part of the cargo under his nominal control. He was going, too.

Jellico was already in the sick bay as Dane came to the door. But neither he nor the medic looked up as the assistant cargo master joined them. They were gazing down rather at an improvised nest in which lay the female brach, inert, so that for an anxious moment or two Dane thought she was dead. There were two small bundles of fur lifting small

37

heads high. Though their eyes were closed, their noses were sniffing as if they were trying to scent some necessary odor.

Dane had seen two very young kits at the lab on Xecho when he had gone to make the arrangements for shipping the pair, but he had not seen them this young. Still, compared with the adult brach they were now nosing, there was something odd about them.

"Mutants?" Was Jellico asking that question of himself or of Tau. "They—well, maybe just after birth they—"

"See here." Tau turned, not to the squirming kits but to a box set at one end of the nest. There was a dial on its surface, and there a needle swung back and forth. "Radiation, radiation. And I can't swear to their being mutants, but it is plain that they do differ from their mother in some ways. There is a bigger brain casing—and they are remarkably alert and active for just-born kits. I'm no vet, and I don't know too much except the general information, but I'd say that they are very well developed for premature births, and they are off their general species pattern."

"Radiation!" Dane caught the word that meant the most to him. He was not given to many flashes of foreboding, insight, or what the emotion might be named that struck him now, but he was sure of disaster. Without another look at the newborn brach he demanded of Tau, "Is that portable?" He pointed to the box in the nest.

"Why?"

But the captain had seemingly caught Dane's train of thought. "If it isn't, we'll have one that is!" He laid hand on the box while the medic stared at them as if they had suddenly developed space fever.

Then Jellico was at the com. "Ya, bring down a planet-side detect!"

With that Tau understood. "Radiation—in the ship! But—"

There were no buts about it as far as Dane was concerned. If what he suspected was true, then all the bits of the puzzle began to fall into place. The stranger would have brought it aboard, hidden it too well for their first search of the treasure hold, and—as Jellico had pointed out—the brach cage was above that.

Now he asked of Tau, "Damaging to the crew?"

"No. I tested for that, though maybe the brachs should be put in isolation. This beam is off known scale—"

"But what of the lathsmer embryos?" Again Dane's speculation followed a logical course, and he was on his way to the treasure hold without waiting to hear Tau's reply.

He pried off the seal he had thought such a protection for their cargo just as the captain arrived, Tau, Shannon, and Ya behind Jellico. Ya held the box meant to be carried on the belt of a planet-side explorer. Tau took it from him and made some adjustment. He had no more than done so when its tell-tale needle began the same swing as the one in sick bay.

They entered the hold. It took only seconds for the detect to show that what they hunted did lie in the direction of the embryo boxes—not among them, nor behind them where they had painstakingly searched earlier, but overhead. Dane jerked out some of the shelf panels not in use and, with that for a ladder, climbed above the containers. Jellico handed him the detect.

It registered wildly at a point on the ceiling, and this close Dane could see scratches there.

"Behind here." He passed down the detect and brought out a small cutter from a belt sling. Not trying to be gentle about the plate, he set to work to pry loose the section that must have been cut out and reset. He gouged at it until it loosened and fell out. There was a pocket there just large enough to hold a box, the box the probe had recalled to his mind.

"Don't touch it with your bare hand!" Tau warned. "Wait for a suit glove."

Rip disappeared to get one, and Dane examined the recess more carefully. The box did not rest on any shelf or hanger. It apparently adhered or was in some way fastened to the ship's plates. Without the detect, they would not have found it. As hasty as the cutting and reclosing of the opening had been, it was skillfully done.

Rip returned, holding up one of the clumsy, well-insulated gloves he had unscrewed from a space suit. Dane wriggled his hand into that and reached up to the box. It adhered all right, as if it had been welded to the metal. For a while as he jerked and pulled, tried to slip it back and forth, he thought they would have to bring a cutting torch to get it loose, perhaps irreparably damaging what it held.

Finally, as he gave it a last corkscrew twist, it came loose, and he brought it out of the hole, holding it well away as he dropped to the deck.

"Get Stotz on this with you," Jellico told Ya. "We don't know what it is, but don't take any chances."

Dane laid it on the deck well away from any cargo, slipped off the glove for Ya to take in turn, and watched the comtech carry the find out, its destination Stotz's workroom.

He no longer worried about the box. It was the condition of the embryos. If the radiation through the decking had had such an effect upon the brachs, what about their most precious cargo? Again Jellico was with him.

"Scanning or sensor examination?" The captain walked around the sealed container, frowning.

"Scanner and sensor both," Tau replied promptly. "I have their correct reading on file. It will be easy to compare."

"Was this aimed at the brachs, the lathsmers, or was it only chance?" Dane asked, though he knew they had no answers for him.

"Not chance!" The captain seemed very sure of that. "If all that was wanted was transportation for that thing, he could have more easily hidden it in your cabin. No, it was put here for a purpose. And I'm inclined to believe it was aimed at the lathsmers."

With that Jellico faced the worst. They had the contract for the mail run, but to have cargo spoilage of such a nature on their first trip might mean black listing for the *Queen*. If they had not discovered the box in time, if radiation-treated lathsmers had been delivered to the settlers who had paid a small fortune for the embryos—? Dane, back at his files, looked into a bleak future. They might find themselves responsible for replacing a cargo worth more than any year's profit. And the *Queen* was not prepared to take such a loss. If they could borrow, to be in debt would automatically break their mail contract, and the result would be ferrying jobs, risky and unrewarding for just as long as they could keep up payments.

I-S? It was the first answer that came to mind. But the *Queen* was so unimportant as far as Inter-Solar was concerned. Sure, they had ruined two I-S plays. But for a com-

pany to go to so much trouble for revenge on a free trader—
he could not agree to that solution.

Dane could not help believing that the answer lay on
Trewsworld. The man wearing his face must have intended
to land there. And the box—maybe the captain was wrong
and the placing of the box was only by chance. They only
needed Tau's report on the state of the embryos to know
the extent of disaster.

The medic did not hurry to give that. He shut himself
up in his lab and was left alone—the crew waiting restlessly
for his verdict.

Stotz, always slow and sure, had his report first. The box
could not be opened, short of disintegration, and it was the
source of steady radiation. When he asked for permission to
breach it by force, Jellico refused. Instead Ali suited up,
went to the fin end of the *Queen*, and planted the thing
against the outer hull of the ship, where it could do, the
engineers decided, the least harm.

When Tau did at last get on the com, it was not to give
them any answers but rather ask for certain of the captain's
collection of xenobiological tapes and a reader. Dane delivered those and caught only a glimpse of the medic as he
opened his door long enough to snatch the material. Then
he closed that portal firmly in the cargo master's face.

They were close to the time to come out of hyper run
when Mura called Jellico to look at the male brach. Dane,
following, saw the steward and the captain kneeling in the
corridor, registering concern.

The animal, which had earlier shown such a determined
and intelligent desire to get free, was now balled in the far
corner of the cage. Untouched food and water were cupped
in the feeder. The sheen that had lightened its body fluff was
gone, and that was matted about its nose as if it had not
tried for some time to clean itself. Nor did it rouse when
Mura chirped to it and showed it a juicy stalk of renton
leaves through the bars.

"Tau had better have a look at it," Jellico said.

Mura was already loosing the extra safeguards on the
cage door. He had that half open and was stretching in a
gentle hand to grasp the plainly sick animal when the brach
came to life. The nose horn flashed, and Mura, with an exclamation, jerked back a hand on which blood ran. Then

there was a scurry, and the brach was out, showing such speed as to avoid them in a way Dane had never seen before.

He ran after it, only to find it at last crouched at the door of the sick bay, using both its horn and its less strong claws in a fruitless attempt to force an entrance there.

Its purpose so consumed it that it did not seem aware of Dane's arrival until he tried to catch hold of it. Then it whirled about and slashed with its horn at his hands, much as it had wounded Mura. It stood on its hind feet, its back to the door it had tried to open, its eyes wild and showing red. Now it began a low, chittering noise, the sounds divided almost, Dane thought, as if it spoke the words of some unknown language.

"The female." Mura came up nursing his torn hand. "It wants to reach the female."

At that moment the door was pushed aside, Tau standing there. The brach was ready, speeding past the medic before the latter was aware of what was going on. As Dane and Jellico pushed forward, they had a glimpse of the brach leaning over the nest box. Now that chittering sound softened. The brach balanced uncomfortably with a third of his small body leaning over the rim, his forepaws stretched down as if it were trying to embrace his mate.

"Better get him," began the captain, but Tau shook his head.

"Let them alone for now. She's been very restless. Now she's quieted down. And we don't want to lose her, too—"

"Too?" questioned Jellico. "The kits then?"

"No. The lathsmer. Look here." He motioned them to the left, well away from the family reunion by the box. There was a viewer on the table, and the medic triggered it. On its small screen flashed a picture, a very vivid one. "That's the present state of the embryo I snooped. Do you understand?"

The captain put his hands on the table and leaned closer to the screen, as if that picture had some vital message. What it did show was a reptilelike creature coiled in a tight package from which it was difficult to separate legs, long neck, small head, or any other portion clearly.

"That's no lathsmer!"

"No, not a modern one. But see here—" Now Tau switched on a record reader, and the tiny, very exact picture it showed was that of a reptilian creature with a long neck, small head, batlike wings, a long tail, and rather weak-appearing legs, as if it depended more upon those wings than upon limbs for a mode of transportation.

"That was a lathsmer ancestor," the medic announced. "No one is sure how many thousand planet years ago. It ceased to exist, as far as our records run, about the time our own ancestors stood reasonably erect and began to use a handy rock for a weapon. We don't have embryos of lathsmers; we have something out of a time so remote that our specialists can't date it."

"But how?" Dane was bewildered. The embryos according to his records were of perfectly normal breeding stock of the most recent well-established mutations, guaranteed to keep on producing the strain without fault. How had they suddenly become these—these dragon things?

"Retrogression!" Jellico stared from one picture to the other.

"Yes," Tau replied. "But how?"

"All of them so affected?" Dane went on to the most important question for him, the present state of the cargo.

"We'll have to test." But Tau's tone was unpromising.

"I don't understand." Dane glanced at the brachs. "You say the embryos retrogressed. But if the intelligence of the brachs increased—"

"That is so." Jellico straightened up. "If the radiation worked one way on these, why a different reaction with the brachs?"

"There could be several reasons. The embryos are just that, not yet completely formed. The brachs were adult creatures when they were exposed."

Dane had another flash of speculation. "Could the brachs have once been a higher type of life? Could they have already retrogressed, so that now they are returned to an intelligent species?"

Tau ran his hands through his short hair. "We could have half a dozen answers, and we can't confirm any without the proper equipment. We'll have to leave that up to the lab techs when we planet."

"But can we?" Jellico absently rubbed the blaster scar on his cheek. "I think we may be in no position to wait upon the opinion of experts, not with settlers who have invested their life savings waiting for lathsmer embryos. Thorson, what was the agreed shipping date for those on the invoices?"

"When transport was possible," Dane replied promptly.

"When possible, no guaranteed date of arrival. Therefore, they could assume that the embryos might come in on the next trip."

"We can't hide those boxes," Tau objected.

"No, not with customs coming on board at setdown. At the same time, this situation is such that I want to appeal to the Board of Trade before I make any other statements."

"You think deliberate sabotage—the I-S, sir?" Dane asked.

"Oddly enough, no. If the I-S saw a chance to score off us in passing, they might do it. But too much planning has gone into this. I think the roots lie on Trewsworld, and I want to know more, much more, before we are any deeper in than we are now. If we show up without the embryo boxes and the brachs, there may or may not be unusual interest shown. That will be our clue to who is behind this, who might protest too loudly if we land without the expected cargo and what they had rigged on board."

"Not jetsam!" Dane protested.

"Not in space, no. But Trewsworld is not a thickly populated world. There is only one main spaceport, and our cargo is consigned there. There will be no sky search if we follow a regular orbit in. So, we load the embryos and the brachs on a lifeboat and set that down in an uninhabited section. Van Ryke, if I can contact him, will have friends on the board. Anyway, I shall ask for a local hearing—in confidence."

But he said nothing of going to the Patrol, Dane noted, spoke only of the one authority the free traders could appeal to, which must mean he wanted none of the formal law until he was sure they had a defense. But a defense against what? As it stood, all of them could go into deep probe and prove their innocence, if that drastic step was needed. It must be that Jellico believed they were in some way involved past the point that even a probe reading could clear them.

"Who takes down the LB?" Tau asked.

Jellico looked to Dane first. "If anyone is expecting your double, he or they won't follow the planned orbit set if you walk out of the *Queen* on landing. We have a dead man on board. He might just as well be the one he claimed to be

44

for a time—Dane Thorson. And we can spare a couple of juniors—Shannon for your pilot—though the LB will home in on automatics, so you won't need to set a course—and Kamil in charge of that infernal box. I want that out of the ship, too, before we fin in at the port. Wilcox will chart you a course that will take you away from any settlement. You'll take a beacon with you and set it on the *Queen's* frequency. Wait a couple of days—then turn it on. We'll contact you when we can."

He turned back to Tau. "What about those embryos? Any of them near decanting time?"

"No way of telling."

"Then the sooner we get rid of them, the better. Mura, get E rations, plus whatever the brachs eat. The LB will be crowded." Jellico spoke again to Dane. "But your ride down won't take long."

Dane culled his own belongings, hoping he was making the right choices as to what he would need. Trewsworld was Terran climate, but it was an untamed world, save for the settlers' holdings spreading out slowly from the port. He took an extra change of clothing in a jump bag, strapped on a belt with the number of small tools carried by a scout, and made sure he had extra charges for his stunner.

As he loaded it, he thought of the brach. Intelligence—retrogressed to a higher form of intelligence? But that would mean the brachs were not really animals at all! The crew of the *Queen* had had one close encounter with ancient Forerunner remains when they had raised the sum to buy at auction trading rights to Limbo.

And Limbo, though partly burned off in some galactic war—traces of which Terran explorers had come across again and again during their travels—had also held a secret that had been as potent in the present day as when its long-vanished makers had first put it into action. There had been a force, operated from a headquarters deep under the planet surface, that had reached into the deeps of space to draw to it any ship venturing within range, so that its half-devastated surface was packed with the wrecks of vessels for centuries of time.

Though modern pirates had found it, made it more predictable, it had been operating on its own for a long time before their coming. Of those who had set it as a defense or assault weapon, no real trace had been left. They had never found a tomb, a space-frozen derelict with bodies on board, any trace of the Forerunners to learn what they had been like. Humanoid or wholly alien—it was any man's guess. However, if the brachs had come to the animal state but had once been intelligent, could they now have on board one answer to the Forerunner riddle?

If that were true—Dane's thoughts leaped—then all the damage done to the embryos was unimportant. The brachs were priceless treasures and ones that the scientists would give much to have. But he could not believe the brachs had been the targets of the man who had planted the box on the *Queen*. He might have meant to destroy the lathsmers, but the opposite effect on the brachs came from the accidental placing of their cage on just the right spot and could not have been foreseen.

5. TEMPORARY TRUCE

They had come out of hyper and were in a breaking orbit around Trewsworld before the last of the preparations was completed. Dane went through a course of instructions as to care of the brachs. The embryo containers had been unlocked from the stacking and packed into the lifeboat. Tau made a spot check on them, only to discover all he tested had been affected by radiation. The box that had caused all the trouble had been inserted in what Stotz believed to be a leak-proof casing and put as far from the cargo and crew of the LB as possible. Ali was under orders to see that it was safely buried in a marked spot as soon after their landing as he could do so.

There was this much in their favor; the LB had built-in safe-guards for its passengers, since it had been devised to protect even injured who managed to reach it, so it had radiation controls as well. And its automatic landing device would bring them in at the best spot its detectors could locate. Now they lay in the hammocks ready for takeoff, the padded brach cage wedged in the narrow aisle, waiting to be ejected from the *Queen*.

The brachs themselves could not be seen. Tau had filled the cage next to the top with any cushioning material he could find, leaving only air holes. As he made the creatures comfortable, he had admitted surprise that the kits, not following the regular pattern of their species, were developing at a rate far faster than normal.

Their parents crouched together, the male's forelegs about his mate as if to shield her from harm, the kits curled at the other end of the box.

Dane had been so rushed with all which must be done that he had not had time to think beyond the task at hand until he was bedded down on the LB. Then he wondered again at Jellico's move in putting the cargo off the *Queen*. Why had the captain been so reluctant to land, report what had happened, and leave the muddle to the authorities? It was almost as if he had foresight and sensed difficulties not apparent to the rest of the crew. But a belief in Jellico was part of the tradition of the *Queen*. If Van Ryke were only here! Dane would have given much to know his superior's reaction.

In general configuration Trewsworld was the opposite of Xecho. Where the aquatic planet with its great seas gave land room only to islands, this was a world of crowding land masses and seas, which were narrow bands hardly wider than rivers, separating one from the other. In climate, too, it differed from the steamy heat of the *Queen*'s other port, being much cooler, with short summers and lengthy winters, during which the ice and snow masses of the poles advanced with grim regularity to threaten the holdings, the small toe-holds off-world settlers had established.

When the LB set down, its small crew were sure of one thing only: that Wilcox's course, fed into an improvised guide on the craft, had brought them to the same continent as the one on which the *Queen* planeted. How far they were from the port, however, they had no idea.

They unstrapped from the hammocks and zipped into thermo jackets, for though it was midday out, it was still well below the temperature they would find pleasant. Shannon triggered the hatch, and they went through the shallow opening into the light.

Xecho had been vivid color—yellow, red, brilliant shades of both those primaries. Here, too, was color, but it was in a different range.

They had earthed on a plateau where there was only a growth of tough grass, now gray and sere, mounded at the nose of the LB where that craft had scored up the lighter layer of soil to cushion its landing. Below was a lake, the water so green that it might have been a Terran emerald of the finest hue dropped into a gray rock setting. On the opposite side from where they now stood was a great wall of glacier overhanging the water. Even as they watched, a huge chunk of ice broke free with a sharp crack and fell into the lake.

Just as the lake was green, a solid opaque green, so was the ice of that creeping wall blue—very, very blue. Yet its rough surface rose here and there in peaks that were frost-white, as if the mass had traveled in waves that had solidified.

The color burst on them and then the quiet. Even when in hyper, there had been vibration in the fabric of the ship, a low purr to which they had long been accustomed and which, in its way, was reassuring to spacemen. Here, save for the noise of that breaking ice, was no sound at all. No wind blew, and Dane, looking to the ice across the water, was glad they did not have to face any blast carried across its frigid surface.

Their landing on top of the plateau was far too open. With any rise of wind they could well freeze unless they stayed in the LB, and that craft was far too noticeable from the air. While Jellico had given them no explicit orders to keep under cover, the fact that he had landed them so was a warning to use common sense and draw no attention to themselves.

They walked back from the lakeside to see what might lie to the south. There was an abrupt drop and then a more gradual slope, covered with dead grass tangles, before the rise of dark brush gave way to trees. Unlike the grass, which had died in the cold, the brush and trees were both thickly leaved, but that vegetation was very dark. Dane could not, from this distance, name it blue, green, gray, or a mixture of all three.

"Can we take her down?" he asked.

Rip looked back at the LB and then to the cliff edge where they stood.

"She's no flitter. But there is some raise power, meant to move her from a dangerous landing. I think it might be enough. What about it, Ali?"

Kamil shrugged. "You can try anything—once," was his unenthusiastic reply. "But the more you lighten her, the better. You lift; we'll see about finding a landing down there."

The cliff face was rough enough to provide them with hand and toe holds. Once he had swung over to join Ali in that descent, Dane discovered that it was far less cold. Perhaps the bulk of the plateau kept some of the icy emanation of the glacier from this side—which was another small point in their favor, since he was sure that the brachs could not survive long in the cold, coming as they did from the much warmer Xecho.

They reached the foot of the cliff and continued on toward the brush, seeking for an opening in the growth into which Rip might be able, with a great deal of luck besides his skill, to maneuver the LB. Dane thought the brush impenetrable directly ahead. He was close enough now to see that the leaves were a very dark blue-green, the colors mottled with sometimes one, sometimes the other, predominant. They were a thick, fleshy growth, marked by patches of gray hair, which also fringed their edges.

Not trying to push into these thickets, Ali turned left, Dane right. Rip waited on the cliff top for a signal as the LB was no hover craft to be held off ground.

The silence continued to grow more menacing as far as Dane was concerned. They had had little time for briefing on the *Queen*, and the instruction tapes about Trewsworld she had carried had naturally, for their purposes, dealt with the port and settlements they might visit in carrying out their duties. There had been little or no information about this wilderness.

But surely life could not be limited to vegetation—yet there were no birds, no flying things, no animals to be sighted. Perhaps the landing of the LB had driven many to cover. Yet he kept hoping to see a single track, some evidence that they were not in a deserted world.

The sound that did break that increasingly ominous silence was a whistle from Ali. He spun around to see Kamil waving to Rip, who disappeared then from sight. Dane did not at once retrace his way. The need to make sure that there was some life here pushed him on a short distance.

What he did find was a bare, black section of ground, unmistakably once the site of a fire. Stones had been set in a rough circle, and in the midst of that lay charred lengths of nearly consumed wood. Sand had been blown across the stones, so that it was plain it had been some time since this campsite had been used. Surveyors from some holding? An exploring party? There might even be a chance that, as on too many frontier worlds, there was an outlaw element here that had taken to the wilderness, though the accounts they had of Trewsworld named it a placid, hard-working, and law-abiding planet.

Dane went a little beyond the campfire and came across unmistakable evidence that the vegetation had been hacked away to clear passage for something larger than a party traveling on foot. In another bare spot that must have been soft clay and was now frozen into a sharp ridged rut, he saw the track of what could only be a crawler. The gashed growth and crushed tracks led on into the shade of the trees.

If they did need a road later on, they might use that track. But for now—

He heard the moan of displaced air and turned in time to see the LB slide from the cliff top and aim in Ali's direction. Not for the first time he admired Rip's skill as a pilot.

They could not hide the marks of their own landing, for the LB smashed a passage into the brush, stopping only when it nosed into the beginnings of the forest. But the growth seemed to possess unusual elasticity, and where it had not been actually broken off, it began to rise slowly and cloak a little of that backtrail.

Why Dane continued to think of some danger in their being seen, he could not explain, save that this whole affair was so bizarre and in a way menacing. And he knew that the captain thought they needed time on their side.

They did not disturb the brach nest-cage. But Ali suited

up and, moving ponderously in that shielded clothing, took the box, to trudge on into the woods. When he came back later, he taped directions as to its burial spot. They could not be sure even now that there was no leakage from the outer shell so hurriedly made in the *Queen*'s engineering repair cabin and that the dire influence of what *was* inside could not spread to the surrounding territory.

"By rights we should have spaced it!" Rip declared as he brought out E-ration tubes and they sat, with their backs to the LB, sucking the contents.

"Space it and you have no chance to pick it up again," Ali returned. "After the captain reports in, there may be a lot of big brains wanting to beam in on it."

"There're the brachs." Dane had been only half listening to them, thinking along another path. "If they have degenerated, well, what's the answer? Are we bound to use the box, or something like it, to return them to an intelligent race? There's the code against interference—how would it work in such a case?"

"Nice legal point." Ali squeezed the last mouthful from his tube and rolled the now flaccid container into a small ball. "If you have a station on a planet marked no *l* life and then you discover you can produce native *l* life there, thus losing your contract, are you required to do just that?"

"You mean Combine might fight any upgrading?" Dane asked. "Is Xecho worth a beam-out with the Council?"

"Xecho," Rip answered, "is a crossroads, a way station. In itself it is not important except for its port. So if the Combine were assured they could keep that, they might not fight upgrading. But it would be chancy. Brachs have been considered harmless, but these have been hostile—"

"Suppose you suddenly woke up to the fact you were a prisoner of an alien race and you had your wife to defend and children—" Ali asked. "What would you do?"

"Just what the brach did," Dane agreed. "So it's up to us, the three of us now, to make contact with the brachs and induce them to see we are friends."

"That we may be able to do. What I don't like is that cargo of embryos," Ali observed. "I think we had better get them out of the ship. They're spoiled now for all purposes. And there's this—the brach gave birth ahead of time. Suppose the radiation works the same way on the embryos, speeds up gestation? Stotz wasn't able to rig any freeze unit to deter that."

"We don't decant them," Dane replied. "If you do, in this cold they'd be finished." But it was only token resistance on his part. With the engineer apprentice, he felt the need for getting those boxes and their nightmare cargo out of the LB. The sooner they were sure that what lay within would never develop further, the better.

It was a wearying business, pulling the boxes out the hatch, tramping among the trees to stack them between two, piling stones around them. The ground here was ankle deep in powdery skeletons of the pulpy leaves, so these must fall at some time. They dug into the dust, using it with the stones to cover the boxes lest some native life try to investigate them, though what manner of tooth, fang, or claw could break them open, Dane had no idea.

The dark had come by the time they had finished, and, tired, they dragged themselves wearily back to the LB, longing for rest in the hammocks. But Dane went first to the brach cage, lifting the lid and pulling aside some of the padding. There was a heaving, and something rose almost under his hand.

A head poked out to regard him with unblinking eyes, by its size one of the kits. However, this was no helpless youngling. He could not mistake the intelligence in that steady gaze, and the fantastic growth rate of the creature astounded him. It was half, maybe two-thirds as big as one of its parents, and might have been a year or more older by brach development. Though the time in hyper followed a different rate than that of planet time, there was nothing to explain this but the effects of radiation.

He was so startled that he was not ready for the next move of the young brach. Showing reaction to their confrontation, the small creature threw itself at the nearest side of the cage, hooked both front paws on the edge, and heaved up with a speed Dane had not seen before—save when the male had gotten out of the cage the second time in the ship.

"Rip—the hatch!"

Shannon jerked the door shut just in time, almost catching the long nose of the infant brach in the crack. Before he could stoop to lay a hand on the escapee, the animal turned and scuttled away, leaping to the nearest hammock, where it settled down, watching them warily, its lip wrinkling back under the horn to show teeth already well budded.

Dane slammed the lid back on the cage just in time, for three more heads had arisen from the padding and other forepaws were reaching for the edge of their prison.

He advanced to the cub in the hammock. "Come on—I won't hurt you. Come on—" he tried to keep his voice low, coaxing, reassuring it as much as he could.

It uttered a high-pitched chittering and tried to horn his hand. But Ali had slipped up behind, using the stuff of the hammock to net it, though he had a struggle on his hands, for the captured one kicked furiously, voicing screeches of mingled fear and rage, which were echoed loudly from the crate. In the end it took all three men to get the kit back with its fellows, and Dane was bitten during that process.

"They have to be fed," he said as he nursed his hand. "And we can't put their food in there until we take out some of the packing—"

"Explain it to them then, nice and slow," Ali suggested.

"But I don't think—"

"All right, I will." Dane interrupted him. Just how intelligent the brachs now were was anyone's guess. He was no specialist in wildlife, but he could not let them go any longer without food or water, and it was plain that if he opened the cage again, he would have a struggle.

He wrapped a plasta strip about his hand to cover the bite and brought out the container of water and the bag into which Mura had packed a supply of brach food. Pouring the water into a shallow bowl, he set it on the deck of the LB, then opened the bag, shaking out into another dish a little of the mixture inside—dried insects, shellfish, and some slightly withered proten leaves—so that they could both see and smell it.

All four heads turned in his direction, and they watched him carefully. All he could do now was to try primitive trade procedures. He touched the water bowl and the heap of mixed food with one hand, then pushed it a little toward the cage.

"Is the hatch closed?" he asked without turning his eyes from the brachs, who met him stare for stare.

"Dogged down," Rip assured him.

"All right. Get back, out of their line of sight if you can."

"How? By melting through the walls?" Ali wanted to know. But Dane heard the click of space boots on the deck and knew that they were moving as well as they could in that tightly confined space.

"You're not going to let them *out?*" Ali demanded a moment late.

"If they are going to eat, I have to. But they ought to be hungry enough to want to get to this more than anything else."

He rose slowly to his knees from squatting on his heels, found the latch of the cover he had just slammed down, and shot it open, moving slowly and with as little noise as he could.

Dane fully expected all four to shoot out the minute the crack was wide enough, with the same speed the kit had shown earlier. But they did not. Still moving with care, he laid the lid all the way back and then inched away himself.

Their regard of him continued for a long moment. Then the kit that had been returned there with such effort made a move. But an adult paw swung, landing on the young nose slightly above horn tip, bringing an indignant squeal of protest. It was the male alone who drew himself up and out of the thick padding. He dropped down beside the food and touched nose to it and to the water pan. Then looking at his family, he made a small muttering sound.

The two kits scrambled over with speed, but the female moved more slowly, and the male returned and balanced on the edge of the cage, chittering to her encouragingly. Now and then he turned his long head to look at Dane and the other two who had backed away as far as they could.

Neither kit had waited for the parents. Both were stuffing eagerly from the food dish, pausing only now and again to lap water, though one liked to put a forepaw into the bowl and lick the moisture from its pads.

Pads? Dane dared not move closer, but he thought that the shape of forepaws for both kits differed from those of the adults—more handlike somehow. When the male had coaxed the female over the edge and to the dishes, he gave several low growls. And the kits, still chewing, one squealing resentfully, backed away so that the male could push his mate forward, standing guard while she—at first languidly and then with a show of greater interest—fed and drank. It was not until she turned away of her own desire that he finished up what remained.

Now what, wondered Dane. They would have to get them back in the cage, though that would probably be a struggle. Just how intelligent were they? And if intelligent, how alien were their thought processes to those of his own species? Intelligence did not always mean ability to communicate.

He would like their cooperation if he could possibly gain it. To use them as animals might only make them ever ready to escape and force the men to be constantly on guard.

Now he tried to echo the small clucking noise the male had used to urge his mate out of the cage. He was successful in that the heads of all four brachs turned in his direction, and he saw that he did have their attention, but there was a tenseness about them that suggested they were ready for instant resistance. Still clucking, Dane moved, careful not to advance toward them. Facing the four, he edged along the wall of the LB, pushing aside the hammocks until he was on the opposite side of the cage from the brachs.

He raised the lid. Instantly all cowered closer to the deck, the male rumbling deep in his throat, the female standing before the two kits, who in turn chittered.

Dane stooped and felt along the edge of the lid. The cage had been improvised, and he hoped not too well. He held the screen up as a barrier between him and the brachs as he worked to loosen the fastenings.

For a space the male continued to rumble. Then when Dane did nothing but work at the lid, he raised a little, manifestly wanting to see what the man was doing. A long moment more, and he jumped to the top of the box, edging along its rim until his head with its useful horn nudged against Dane's fingers. The man jerked back in surprise, and straightway the horn fitted under the fastening and pried away until the hinge was loose and off. Then the brach swayed along the rim and followed through with the other. Dane lifted the cover away and stood back, uncertain as yet as to whether this gesture could be understood, though the brach's aid with the fastening was promising.

The male brach continued to teeter on the rim of the cage, looking from Dane to the lid, now resting against the cabin wall. Dane dared to move, sidling around the cage, still leaving what he trusted would be a reassuring distance between him and the brachs. Then he stooped and pulled at the padding, pulling it out in chunks, until he left only enough to form what he hoped would be acceptable bedding. The brach balanced, still watching.

Then the female brach moved, pulling up and over into the cage. She reached with forepaws and teeth to catch the last puff of padding Dane had loosened, drawing it determinedly out of his grasp and thumping it down with force on the floor of the cage. She called to the kits, who obeyed her, to Dane's relief. And lastly the male brach jumped down to curl up with his family. Dane stepped away.

"Does that mean that they are willing to stay if they aren't shut in?" Rip wondered.

"We can hope so. But we'll have to keep the hatch locked. It is too cold out there." Dane pushed the extra padding along the floor. Suddenly he was so tired that he felt he could not make another effort, no matter how needful, as if his struggle to communicate with the brach had been in some way as harrowing an ordeal as the one on Xecho. He wanted peace and quiet and sleep, and he only hoped that was what they could depend upon—with no more complications for a while.

6. MONSTER FROM THE PAST

"Rise and orbit!"

Dane was jarred out of sleep, his hammock oscillating from a hearty push Rip must have delivered, for Shannon still had a hand raised as if to shove again if his first assault was not effective. Dane sat up groggily. For a second or two he was not oriented. This was not his cabin on the *Queen*.

Beyond Rip, as he was able to focus better, he saw Ali wearing a thermo jacket, already at the hatch as if impatiently awaiting him.

"What's the—?"

"We may have trouble," Ali answered. "See?"

He pointed. Ali had made certain safeguard arrangements when they had completed their two caches—that of the box and that of the embryos. He had set small ray warns on each so that any disturbance would be recorded on an improvised pickup, and now one was blinking red with warning enough to shake Dane fully out of sleep.

"Which one?" With their present luck it would be the box, of course. He swung stiffly out of the hammock and reached for his own thermo wear.

But Ali surprised him. "The embryos. Fire rockets, can't you—this is a speed job!"

They came out into the early morning and a crisp chill, which made Dane pull up his hood with its visored face plate and tuck his hands into the gloves, which dangled at the ends of his sleeves, but he remembered to make fast the hatch, insuring that the brachs were safe in the warm cabin.

There was a rime of frost on twigs and leaves, giving a silvery coating to the vegetation, and their breath formed small white clouds.

"Listen!" Rip threw up his hand as if to bar them from entering the path they had made yesterday when dragging the containers to the cache.

They heard a crackling, as if something large forced its way through the brush. There was another noise, a kind of snort sounding now and then, and from that they judged that whatever might be sniffing around was no small creature.

Dane drew his stunner, thumbed its controls to full force, and saw that his companions were doing the same. The growth hid whatever crunched along, and they could only trace it by sound. But by the sound it was going away, not coming toward them. They stood listening for several minutes until they were sure the unknown had retreated farther into the wood.

That it had been nosing about the embryos' cache Dane was sure. Perhaps there was some scent that attracted it. They had best see how much damage it had done. The lathsmers were useless to the settlers—that was positive—but no cargo could be destroyed until ordered, and Dane did not have that order. Therefore, he must protect the boxes until he did.

They had not gone far along the tracks left by their journey of the day before when they came to the signs left by the other thing. It had tramped, or rather stomped. There were prints breaking the frozen crust of the ground, large enough so that when Dane knelt to measure his hand beside them, the marks spread beyond the stretch of his fingers. They were not very plain, for the frostbound soil had resisted even this heavy weight. They were more like rounded holes than anything else.

A stunner set on high would take care of most creatures, but there were on some worlds menaces with nervous systems on which such a ray would have no more effect than the flick of a twig. Then a blaster was the only answer, but those they did not have.

So now they went slowly, listening, relying on the fact the crashing was faint and the unknown was still going from them. When they came to where they had hidden the containers, they had more proof of the strength of what they had not yet seen, for the stones and earth they had piled with such backbreaking effort to hide the cache had been pulled away. The containers themselves had been battered and broken, though they had been made to withstand all the shocks and strains that might occur during space flight. They were twisted and rent, and two had been opened as if they had been as easy to handle as an E-ration tube.

And as an E-ration tube would have been by a hungry man, they had been completely emptied. Dane kicked one out of the way to see a third that had been bent and then left. He had not been mistaken. What had rested so cushioned inside was stirring. But it was not time for it to be decanted yet! As with the brachs, its "birth" was coming ahead of schedule.

He could see the writhing of the monster body inside. A few more minutes and it could certainly die. Since it was a monster, let it. Only his sense of duty objected. Cargo intact—that was what it said. And perhaps it would be proof of their own innocence to keep these embryos intact until the techs could assess what had happened to them.

But this scaled, half-serpent thing—they could not nurse it in the LB. And how long before Jellico sent them instructions?

Dane knelt beside the broken container. Surely the thing would be frozen stiff soon. Reptiles were especially sensitive to extremes of both cold and heat. Perhaps they could freeze it and keep it that way, as they had kept the body of the dead stranger on the *Queen*.

What had seemed feeble struggles at first were growing stronger instead of weaker. If the thing felt the cold, the chill stimulated it to greater efforts instead of sending it into stupor and death. The container shook back and forth now under the wriggling and fell over on its side. Through the rent in the top, not large enough for the creature to crawl through, was thrust a scaled foot, large claws gouging at the frost-filled ground for purchase to pull itself out.

Dane changed the reading on his stunner to half and rayed the container. The clawed foot released its clutch on the soil and relaxed. The container ceased rocking.

"Two more want out." Ali had been stacking the containers. Now he indicated two set to one side.

These had not been misused by the feaster. However, before the men could move, now the tops swung open as they were triggered to do at "birthing," and the things inside began to crawl out. Rip beamed them unconscious.

Dragon heads on long necks swung limply over the edges of their boxes.

"How about the others?" Dane went to check. But there were no more signs of life. The warning tags on the covers were safely blank.

"What do we do? Give them full beam and finish them off?" Ali asked.

Probably the most sensible move. But they were cargo, and they might be needed. Dane said as much and saw Rip nod slowly as if he agreed.

"The labs might want them. Maybe they could tell more about the radiation by examining them. But where do we put them?"

"Yes, where?" Ali demanded. "The LB? If so, we'd better move out. It's turned into a part-time zoo already. And these" —his nose wrinkled—"are not the best shipmates. At least they don't smell fresh—"

Certainly the fetid odor of the inert reptiles made them the last things one wanted penned under or around one's bed. But they would never live outside unless some kind of a heated pen could be rigged. Dane wondered about that aloud.

"We have the brach cage. If they cooperate as they did last night," Rip suggested, "we can put them in the extra hammock. And these containers, could we pound them out and weld them around the cage with a heat unit hooked up?"

Ali picked up one of the smashed containers. "Can't promise anything, but it's worth trying. At least we can't share the LB with them loose or in boxes either. That stink's enough to send one's stomach into space. How long will they stay under?"

Dane did not want to touch the unconscious things, and he had no way of judging. The only answer was that one of them would have to stay on guard while the other two worked.

"There's another problem," Rip said, and it was not the kind of thought to add brightness to their day. "That thing that smashed in here might have acquired a taste for pseudo lathsmer. If it trails or hunts by scent, it might follow to the LB. Do we want that?"

That made sense, Dane thought. His first solution had been to get the creatures back to the craft and build the heated pen right outside. But did they need to do that?

Ali responded to the same idea. "We could set up a nasty jolt for anything that did come hunting," he offered. "Stotz gave me a tool kit when we left, and we can run a wire from the ship and set up a force field—"

Dane was willing to trust to Ali. Anyone who held a cadet's berth under Johan Stotz knew his business, and it would not be the first time that a free trader crew improvised. Half their wandering life depended upon imaginative thinking when confronted by a crisis.

So that long day was spent in hard labor—Ali providing the information and technical knowledge they must have, Rip and Dane giving untrained labor. They straightened out the three containers the strange hunter had mauled and two others whose tabs reported the contents dead, throwing the misshapen embryos those had held into a pit and rolling stones over them, well away from where they proposed to build the pen.

In the end they had a somewhat lopsided-looking structure that should be large enough to house the three still sleeping creatures, and this fitted about the brach cage stripped of all its contents. Ali rigged his force field, warning them that they were thus exhausting the power of the LB.

The brachs appeared perfectly content to be transferred to the fourth hammock in the cabin. In fact, they slept away much of the day, and Dane wondered if they were, in the natural state, nocturnal, reminding himself to be sure to dog down the hatch door that night just in case they took a fancy to wander.

They did not leave the dragon pen by the rest of the containers. Those they restacked and recovered with many more stones. In the bargain, Ali cut down three fairly good-sized trees and dragged them so that their thick upper branches met and tangled about the cache.

The pen they set closer to the LB, using the saw to clear the underbrush not only around the site they chose but also in a cutting back to the LB, so they were given a clear path to it, should need arise.

Dane had no idea as to what food the mutants would eat. Judging by their teeth, they might be carnivores. So his offering was a panful of squeezed out E-rations, which he left for the creatures when they awakened from the stunner-induced sleep. If they ever did—for it seemed to him that their day-long sleep was ominous, though it made their own task that much easier.

Ali rigged an alarm to awaken them if the pen was approached during the night. They were all almost too tired to eat as they settled in their hammocks for the night. Dane checked the door before he went to his. There had been stirring among the brachs, but he had left out food and water. He only hoped that if they did go roaming, they would be considerate enough to avoid waking the human members of the crew, but there was a small nagging worry in his mind, as a hint of toothache might come and go before a final explosion of pain in the jaw. The brachs had been too quiet, too cooperative during the day. He wondered if they were laying plans of their own.

The fact that it was freezing cold out might deter them

from exploration, even if they could master the locking system set up on the hatch door. He did not believe they would really venture out. He was so tired that even the prick of worry could not keep him awake.

Cold—bitter, bone-reaching cold. He was buried in the glacier looking down into the emerald lake, but the cold was a part of him. He must move, must break the film of ice, gain his freedom—or else he would slide, still in the core of a block, to be lost forever in green water depths. He must break loose. He made a mighty effort.

Under him the block swung and shook. It was giving away—he was falling into the lake! He must get free—

The jar of landing on the deck of the LB, the hammock twisted over him, brought Dane awake. He was shivering still with the cold of his dream. But it wasn't from his dream! Cold air did sweep over him. He scrambled to his hands and knees, and in the very subdued light of a single rod over the controls, he saw the hatch door partly open and heard the moan of the wind outside.

The brachs! He shut the hatch first and then turned to the hammock where they had bedded down the aliens. As he expected, that was empty. Only the pile of bedding from their cage lay there, though he wasted a moment to pull that aside, hoping to find them cuddled under it.

He still had that in his hand when the buzz of the warning Ali had rigged sounded loudly through the LB. If the hunter had sniffed them out, the brachs could not only be in the freezing cold but helpless before that menace!

Dane grabbed his thermo jacket even as he saw Rip and Ali begin to pull out of their hammocks.

"The brachs are gone," he told them tersely, "and the cage alarm is on." He need not have added that, with its buzz punishing their ears in that confined space.

He picked up a hand beamer and snapped it to the fore of his belt, leaving his hands free. The brachs rather than the dragons must be their first concern. Outside the LB it was as cold as he had feared. By his timer it was well past midnight, into the early morning hours. The low ray of his beamer—for he kept it to the low cycle—picked up marks in the frost, not well defined, but which he thought were brach tracks. He could only hope that the thick wall of brush had kept them to the path for a swift escape.

Dane heard the hatch clang shut and knew that the others must be on his heels, but he tried to walk as noiselessly has he could and with what speed the night, the low light, and the rough ground would allow. Luckily they did not have too far to go, always supposing that the brachs had been entrapped in the force field Ali had set by the dragon cage.

Though Dane might be going carefully, there was something ahead that sought no such progress. The thud of the same ponderous tread they had earlier heard was loud.

So the hunter had come back in search of the embryos. Now, as Dane half hesitated, holding his stunner at full charge but ignorant of what protection it would be against an alien life form, he heard a cry—shrill, rising in ululation of fear. And though he had not heard a brach scream before, he was very sure that had come from one of their throats.

Dane snapped the beamer to full and ran, the magnetic plates on his boot soles waking a hollow echo on the frozen ground. It was only seconds before he burst into the clearing they had made for the cage. Around it blazed the haze of the force field. Within that tenuous defense crouched the brachs. One of the kits lay on the ground, its brother or sister huddled against it, while, with their heads down to present nose horns to the enemy, the two adults stood guard.

It was a pitiful guard, for that which confronted them might have smashed both into bloody paste with a single swipe of one of its six limbs. It reared high, bracing itself back so that its rounded abdomen touched the ground, four limbs serving as a ship's cradle to anchor it there, while it swung its smaller torso and its long front arms back and forth before the force screen.

Apparently it was wary of that, for it did not try to touch the haze, but the strangeness of the attacker startled Dane into momentary immobility. Ant–beetle? No, it had no hard overskin such as those insects possessed. Instead it was covered, over rounded paunch, back, and thorax with long fur of hair of grayed-black, matted and filled with twigs and leaves, until it almost resembled one of the bushes moving, supposing its head, those waving forelimbs, and its aura of malignancy might be disregarded.

The upper limbs ended in long, narrow, toothed claws,

which it constantly opened and shut, making swift darts with them at the force field, though it seemingly still hesitated to reach into that. Dane took aim on the round head in which the fore part was largely covered by great faceted eyes, another insectile resemblance.

The head shook as his stun beam must have caught its center. Then the thing looked down, over its shoulder at an angle he would not have thought possible for any living thing with a backbone or skeleton to assume.

One of the clawed forelimbs swung, but Dane grimly stood his ground, continuing to pour the full strength of the stun beam at its head. However, its actions were such that he feared he had chosen the wrong way to knock it out. Did it carry what brain it had somewhere else in that monstrous body? Ali and Rip, seeing that Dane's attack did not knock it out, aimed lower, one at the thorax, the other at the barrel abdomen. Some one of the three must have reached a vital part, for the flailing limbs fell, to flap feebly a time or two against the body. It shuffled half around, as if attempting to flee, and then crashed, missing the dragon cage and the beleaguered brachs by only a little.

Ali snapped off the force field, and they hurried to the smaller creatures. Three were unhurt, but the kit lying on the ground had a tear along its shoulder down to its ribs, and it whimpered pitifully as Dane bent over it, the rest of the family drawing back as if they knew he meant to help.

"The dragons"—Ali had gone to peer into the cage—"are gone. Look here!" Under his touch the door swung open as if they had never latched it. But Dane would have taken an oath that they had.

He gathered up the kit with all the gentleness he could and started back for the LB, the other three brachs close behind him, chittering those sounds that, the more one heard them, sounded like words.

"We'll look for the dragons," Rip said, "if you can manage."

"I can." Dane wanted to get the brachs back to the warmth and safety of the LB. Neither Ali nor Rip would take chances with the stunned monster he knew. The first thought must now be for the wounded brach.

Whether remedies intended for humans would heal the wounded kit, he had no way of being sure, but those were all he had to use. So he sprayed the wound with antibiotics, painted it with a thin coat of plasta-heal, and settled the small body in the hammock where its mother speedily joined it, pulling it gently against her and licking its head until its eyes closed and apparently it slept.

The male brach and the other kit still squatted on the shelf where they had all climbed to watch Dane at his doctoring. Now, as he put away the med-kit, the cargo master looked at them. That they seemed able to speak to one another was evident. Could they communicate with him or he with them? There was one provision that was regular equipment on an LB and that he might try. He went to one of the emergency storage pockets and brought out a box, taking up its contents with care. There was a small mike, a voice box to strap to his own throat, and a flat disk. The second set of throat mike and strap he put to one side. Then he set the disk before the male brach.

"I, Dane—" He tried the oldest of all approaches, giving his own name. "I, friend—"

His hopes were so far realized that a series of squeaks did come from the disk. But whether the subtle speech translator had indeed made clear that limited reassurance he could not tell.

The male brach made a startled sidewise leap that almost took it completely off the shelf, and the kit screeched, jumping for the hammock, huddling down beside the female. Her nose had come up to present the horn, her lips drawn back in a warning snarl.

But the male did not retreat any farther. Instead, he hunkered down, looking from Dane to the disk, as if he were analyzing the problem. He hitched closer, watching Dane. The man tried again.

"I, friend—"

This time the chittering did not startle the brach. He advanced to lay a forepaw on the disk, then touched its short antenna wire, looking from that to the mike against Dane's throat.

"My hand, it is empty. I, friend—" Dane moved with infinite care, holding out his hand, palm up and empty as he had said. The brach bent forward, advanced its long nose, and sniffed.

Dane withdrew his hand, got slowly to his feet, brought out the food mixture, and filled the bowl. "Food," he said distinctly. Water was poured into the container. "Water, to drink—" He set them both where the brach could see them.

The female brach called out, and her mate scooped up the food dish, taking it to her. She sat up in the hammock, dipping up some of the mixture, licking it from her paw, pushing more into the mouth of the injured kit, who had also roused. The male took a long drink before he carried the water to those in the hammock, but he did not remain with his family. Instead he leaped once more to the shelf by the disk. Now he squatted with his snout very close to it, chittering at some length. He had the idea, at least half of it, Dane exulted. Now, could he get him to wear the other throat mike so the translator would work both ways? Before he could reach for it, the hatch opened. The male scuttled away from the disk and plumped into the hammock, and Dane turned, with some exasperation, to face Rip and Ali.

At sight of their expressions his attempt to communicate with the brachs was no longer of first importance.

7. ICEBOUND MURDER

"How large was the thing we stunned?" Ali asked. He made no move to unseal his tunic, and he still carried his stunner ready as if prepared to fight off an attack.

"Taller than any of us." Dane could not give a more concise measurement. What difference did the size of the thing make? It was a menace, but they had proved stunners could handle it.

"By rights"—Rip had holstered his weapon and now measured in the air another distance, about a foot between his two hands—"it should be no bigger than this, and, well, there are other differences, too."

"Suppose you say what you mean, loud and clear." Dane was in no mood for any more puzzles.

"On Asgard"—Ali took up the explanation—"there's a burrowing creature, not too different really from a Terran ant, except in size and the fact that it does not live in colonies but is solitary. Only it doesn't grow hair or fur, and it is not able to decapitate a man with its claws or stamp him flat. They call it—the settlers do—an antline. What we met out there is an antline with embellishments."

"But—" Dane began a protest when Rip cut in.

"Yes, but and but and but! We're both sure that was—is —an antline with modifications, just as the embryos were modified, just as these brachs are not running true to type."

"Then the box—" Dane's thoughts leaped to the danger they had buried. Stotz's guard must not have been secure. The radiation had worked again on some creature burrowing too near its hiding place.

Rip might have been reading his thoughts. "Not the box," he said flatly. "We went to look. It's undisturbed. Also that thing could not have altered overnight to its present form. We did a little backtracking. It's been here since before we set down."

"What proof have you of that?"

"A lair burrow." Alie's face mirrored his distaste. "Complete with the refuse. No, it's plainly been that size and been resident there for a good deal longer than two days. But it's an antline."

"How can you be so sure? You say there are superficial resemblances between a Terran ant and the antline. There could well be a native animal or insect here with the same general conformation, could there not? And this has differences—you say so yourself."

"Rational reasoning," Ali replied. "If there was not a museum of natural history on Asgard, and if it hadn't happened that we had a shipment for it some voyages back, some Fortian artifacts that Van Ryke wanted given special handling, we wouldn't know. While the curator was signing off our responsibility, we did some looking around. There was an earlier type of antline that died off long before the first settlers arrived. But some got caught in flash floods, were buried deep in peat, and were preserved. Those were large, haired, and enough like that thing out there to be its loving brother or sister! Asgard being a goodly number of parsecs from here, how do you explain the transportation of

67

a living life form that died out on another world about fifty thousand planet years ago?"

"The box—" Dane kept returning to the only rational explanation. But from that it was easy to take the next step. "Another box?"

Rip nodded. "Not only another box, but surely an importation of other life forms. There is no duplication of such an animal from one world to the next. So, someone imported a modern antline, gave it the retrogressive treatment, and produced that thing. Juast as we have the dragons—"

"The dragons!" Dane remembered the missing cargo. "Did it eat them?"

"No—little one—freed them—" The words were high pitched with a metallic undernote. Dane stared at his two companions. Neither one of them had said that. And they, in turn, were looking at a point behind him as if they could not believe in what they saw. He turned his head.

Once more the male brach hunched on the shelf where he had sat to listen to the chittering of Dane's voice out of the disk. But now the alien had something in his forepaws, pressed against his throat—the translator.

"Little one freed them." The brach was certainly speaking, and the words issuing from the disk made sense. "He was curious, and he thought that it was not right—those things in our home. They hurt him when he opened cage. He called—we went to him. The great thing came, but the dragons were already gone into the woods. This is so."

"By the brazen hoofs of Kathor!" exclaimed Ali. "It's talking!"

"With the translator!" Dane was almost as startled. He had left that other throat mike some distance away. The brach must have gone after it, working out that Dane's was what made the man's voice intelligible, and was now using it. But what a gigantic upstep in intelligence that action revealed—unless the brachs had never been truly the animals they had seemed and the radiation box had not as far back to take them as the Terrans believed.

"You talk." The brach indicated the mike it held pressed to its throat and then pointed to the disk. "I heard. I talk, you hear. This is true. But the dragon things not eaten by the big one. They were big also—too big for cage place.

68

Pushing on wall, clawing door— Little one thought they be too tight, open to give them room. They fly—"

"Fly?" Dane echoed. It was true the creatures had flapping skin appendages that would in the far future be the wings of the lathsmers. But that they could use them for flying—!

"We have to get them back, and if they are flying in the woods—" he began when the brach added:

"They do not fly good, many times on ground—hop, hop—" He gestured with his free paw to represent progress in a jerky manner.

"They could be anywhere," Rip said. The brach looked to him questioningly, and Dane realized the alien could understand only when Dane spoke with the translator.

"They could have gone in any direction," he repeated for the alien.

"Seek water—need water—" the brach replied. "Water there—" He pointed now to the south, as if he could see pond, lake, or streams through the solid wall of the LB.

"But the lake is in that direction." Rip nodded to the northwest, where it lay behind the plateau.

"That direction—lake," Dane translated.

"No, not go there—but there!" And again the alien waved to the south.

"You see them?" Ali asked. Then realizing that Dane alone could voice the question, he added, "Ask him why he is so sure."

But Dane had already begun. If the long-snouted face with its so alien features could have mirrored the emotion surprise, Dane believed he would be reading it. Then the brach's paw touched that part of his head that would be a human forehead and answered, "The dragons want water bad, so we feel—feel the want—"

"Telepathy!" Rip almost shouted.

But Dane was not sure. "You feel what thing thinks?" He hoped that was clear.

"Not what thinks, only what other brach thinks—sometimes. What thing feels, we feel. It feels strong, we know."

"Emotional broadcast of some kind," Ali summed up.

"Little one feel dragons want out, so let them," continued the brach. "Then dragon hurt little one. A thing of badness—"

"The cold," Rip said. "If they went hunting water to the south, the cold will get them."

"So we have to find them first," Dane answered.

"Someone has to stay for the com," Ali pointed out.

"Pilot does that," Dane said swiftly before Rip could protest. "We take travel coms with us. You can signal us back if you have to."

He expected a protest from Shannon, but the other was already hauling out packs, opening the storage cabinets for supplies. It was the brach who spoke.

"Go with. Can feel dragons—tell where—"

"Too cold," Dane returned quickly. He might have lost part of the cargo, but the brachs were infinitely more important than the hatched embryos, and he was not going to risk them.

"I don't know." Rip held one of the supply bags. "Put a small heat unit in this, cut to low, pack our friend in with that"—he nodded toward the padding they had stripped out of the cage—"and he would be warm enough. What he says makes sense. If he can give you a guide to the dragons, you could save a lot of time and energy."

Dane took the bag from Rip. It was watertight, pressurized in part, meant to carry supplies on wholly inimically atmosphered planets, another of the save-life equipment of the LB, and it was certainly roomy enough to hold the brach, even with the warming factors Rip had listed. If what the brach boasted was the truth—that he could keep in touch with the lathsmer changelings by some kind of emotional direction finder—then his company would keep them from losing time. And Dane had the feeling, which grew stronger every time he left the LB, that the sooner they were out of this wilderness, the better.

Ali's trained hands carried out Rip's suggestion. A small heat unit went into the bottom of the bag, and the padding was wrapped around and around the sides, leaving a center core in which the brach could be inserted. The shoulder straps on the side could be easily lengthened to fit Dane, while Ali himself could carry the other supply bag. They each had a personna com clipped to the hoods of their jackets, and in addition Dane's translator was fastened close to his cheek in his.

The brach had gone to his family in the hammock, and

from the subdued murmur there Dane guessed he was explaining his coming absence. If there were protests from the others, Dane was not to know, for the male had left the translator to be affixed in the bag.

It was midmorning when they set out, taking the path back to the cage. The door swung open, and the antline, if mutated antline the thing really was, had gone. Marks, deep grooved in the ground, suggested that it had crawled rather than walked to the eastward.

"Lair is that way," Ali observed. "I think that the lie out in the cold for so long didn't do it any good. At least you can hear it coming."

"If it is an antline returned to an earlier form—" Dane still found it difficult to accept that.

"Then who brought it here and why?" Ali ended his question for him. "That is something to think about. I believe we can assume that ours was not the first box, also that they were too hurried over shipping this one. Looks almost as if they were being rushed in some way. The Combine didn't have any trouble on this mail run. Which means if another box came through, it was better shielded, or else there was no live cargo to cause suspicious complications. And that I can't believe. The settlers have regular embryo shipments, not only of lathsmers, but other livestock."

"They may not be using regular transportation—whoever 'they' are," Dane pointed out.

"True. There's only one main port here, and they don't keep a planet-wide radar system. There's no need for it. There's nothing here to attract any poachers, jacks, or smugglers—or is there?"

"Drugs," ventured Dane, supplying the first and easiest answer, some narcotic easily raised in virgin ground, a small, light cargo bringing a fantastic return for growers' and suppliers' trouble.

"But why the box? Unless it is used to force growth in some way. Drugs might be the answer. If so, we may be facing some blaster-happy jacks. But why import an antline and turn it into a monster? And why did that dead man come on board wearing your face? That seems more like a frame for the *Queen*. I can suggest a good many different solutions—"

71

"Water ahead—" The pipe of the brach rang in Dane's ear.

"Do you sense the dragons?" Dane attended to the matter now at hand.

"Water—no dragon now. But dragon needed water."

"If he doesn't pick them up," Ali commented when Dane passed on this information, "they may be already dead."

Dane shared the other's pessimism. They now threaded a way among the trees, their boots sinking into a decayed mass of fallen leaves. The brush, which had been like a wall before, was gone, and the land sloped downward.

Glancing back, Dane could see the marks of their trail plainly. They would not have to be beamed back to the LB but simply retrace that.

The brach's water came into sight, almost too suddenly for their own safety, for the ground was cut by a giant slash, and they stood on the brink of a very deep and steep-walled gully through which wound a stream.

"Outflow of the lake," Ali said, squinting along the direction from which it flowed.

Well out from the shores, it was encased in ice, but in the middle was a clear channel, where they could see a swift—very swift—current passing from northeast to southwest. There was no sign of any frost-bitten or frozen dragon.

"Do you feel them now?" Dane asked of his alien burden.

"Not here. Away—beyond—"

"Which way?" Dane tried to pin that very vague direction to something definite.

"Over water—"

If they had crossed that river, they had indeed taken to wing. There was no other way of crossing. Dane could not understand how they had continued to survive the cold unless they were far less susceptible to the frigid climate than he supposed. Now it remained for him and Ali to find some place where the banks of the gulch could be descended, where the stream itself could be bridged. Within sight there was no such place.

They separated, Ali going northeast toward the lake, Dane southwest. But the river remained much the same until Dane came to a place where there was a break in the bank on his side. The thing that had gouged that was at river level, slewed around, trapped in the thick ice of the stream edge, the lip of the swift current tearing at it, sending spray to give it a further icy coating.

A crawler—made for heavy duty on rough land! There was no one to be seen in the cabin. He had not expected to find a driver, since the indications were that the vehicle had been there for some time, but he skidded down the broken bank to look it over.

Short of getting tackle as strong as that used at a port, Dane believed there was no chance of bringing this battered machine from its present bed. Perhaps if the river rose high enough, it might tear it loose and roll it on. That the crawler could be of any service to them he doubted.

It was not an agricultural machine with the various attachments used in farming. Instead, it mounted a small borer, now knocked askew, and the battered remains of a digger. This was a mining machine, or at least one for a prospector on a very small scale. In hopes it might give him some clue to a near camp or settlement, Dane worked his way cautiously out on the rough ice that had frozen about its treads to hammer at the cabin door.

When he forced that open at last, he wished he had not, for the cabin was occupied after all, though its occupants had fallen out of sight, lying on the floor, one above the other. Both men had been blaster-burned. There was a strip of ident plate on the fore of the controls, and very gingerly Dane worked that out of its slot. When—if—they returned to the port, this might give some aid in solving these deaths—these murders.

He closed the door, wedging it the tighter with chunks of ice to lock it. But before he left, Dane opened the supply compartment. The rations might be of some use to them, though he could not carry them now, but it was what lay in the transport bin he wanted most to see. They had been killed. Had that bin been plundered?

His hunch was right. The seal on that compartment had been burned out, and the door hung half melted. It was empty, save for a single small piece of rock stuck in the edge of the broken door, as if it had been caught there when someone swept the contents out in a hurry.

The piece of rock was small enough to take along with the ident, and if it had been valuable enough to keep behind a seal lock, it must have some meaning.

73

Dane had no way of judging how long the crawler had been here, but he thought by the ice that had locked around it, it had been some time. As he climbed to the top of the cliff down which the machine had dug its way, he backtracked a little. The trail left there ran parallel with the cliff rim for a short space before the plunge down, which might mean that the descent had not been an attempt to flee across river but that the machine had been running off automatics, already carrying a dead crew when it went.

Was this the same machine that had left the marks below the plateau? It was likely, only he was not to be sidetracked any longer to find out.

"Calling Thorson! Calling Kamil!" The signal was so sharp from his com that he started. "Return to LB, return to LB —at once!"

It was unlike Rip to be so formal—unless some emergency warranted that formality as a warning. The antline? Or, thought Dane, turning back on his trail at a steady trot and looking down at the crawler as he passed, had they two-legged enemies as well? Could those who had blasted the prospectors have turned their attention now on the spacecraft? Was Rip in such a position that he could not warn them save through his choice of words?

The brach made no sound. If the alien sensed trouble ahead as he had been able to sense the dragon's actions, he was not saying so. Suddenly another thought crossed Dane's mind, and it was almost as startling as that summons from the ship because it presented what was an impossibility as far as he knew. When they had found the brachs at bay before the antline, they had been *inside* the force field, a barrier that had kept the monster uneasy and unwilling to make an attack. And the dragons had been gone, also through that field. It had been a weak one, yes, but Ali had tested it, and it had worked. Then how had both species managed to pierce it?

"When the little one"—Dane spoke into the translator— "found the cage, there was a protection around it. Yet he went in, opened the door for the dragons—" Could he make the brach understand, or what *had* happened to the field? Had the aliens turned it off and then on again? They could turn it off if they had understood it. But to turn it on again from the inside was impossible.

The answer came hesitatingly as if the brach was also finding it difficult to explain a process he had taken for granted or else had not the proper vocabulary to make himself understood. "We think—if a thing is not alive, we can think what we wish to do, and it does that—"

Dane shook his head. If the brach meant what he said—that they had some control over the inanimate, some esper control— But the proof was that they had gone through the defense field. And the dragons, but it couldn't be that the dragons could also do that?

"The dragons, how did they get through the protection?"

"The little one—when they hurt him—he opened it for them. They wished to go, so they used it," the brach replied with prompt logic.

Well, it all fitted, if you were willing to accept the initial proposition that the brachs could think an open door through a force field. There was more and more to these mutated animals—no, they were not animals—these people (you must give them their proper status no matter what they had been on Xecho) than one could understand. What excitement they were going to cause when the scientists and lab techs learned about them.

Dane saw Ali coming on the run and slowed to a stop until the other joined him.

"Listen." Dane pushed the brach question to the back of his mind as he quickly gave Kamil the story of the derelict crawler and what it contained.

"So you think Rip may have visitors?" Ali caught him up swiftly. "All right, we go in slowly and carefully."

Both of them had been rubbing their mikes with a gloved thumb as they talked, so that none of what they said could be picked up by a listener. Now Dane was glad to pull down his visor against the frosty chill. Though there was a sun in the sky, it gave little warmth even here in the open, and as they passed into the shade of the wood again, even that illusion of light and heat was lost.

Approach the LB with caution they did. But when they saw what stood a little beyond it in the open, they were less suspicious. There was no mistaking the scout flitter of the *Queen*. Dane felt a warm wash of relief. So Jellico had sent for them—maybe they were now on the verge of solving the whole tangle. Reassured, they trotted on to the hatch.

Rip was inside, and Craig Tau, but the third man was not the captain as Dane expected, nor any member of the *Queen*'s crew. And Rip's expressionless face, as well as Tau's stiff stance, was warning that they were not at the end of their troubles.

The stranger was of Terran stock but somewhat shorter than the crewmen, wide of shoulder and long of arm, both of which were accented by the bulk of the fur upper garment that he had unsealed but not taken off. Underneath he wore a green tunic of a uniform with a badge on the breast consisting of two silver leaves springing from a single stem.

"Ranger Meshler, Dane Thorson, acting cargo master, Ali Kamil, assistant engineer." Medic Tau made the formal introduction and added an explanation for his crewmates. "Ranger Meshler is now in charge in this district."

Dane moved. He might not be right in his sum-up of the present situation, but one of the lessons of infighting that most free traders knew was to get an enemy or possible enemy off balance, to deliver the first blow and make it as unexpected a one as possible. "If you represent the law here, I have a murder, two murders, to report."

He pulled out the ident strip from the crawler and the fragment of stone he had found caught in the plundered lock bin. "There is a crawler by the river, caught in the ice. I think it has been there for some time, but I don't know enough of your planet conditions to guess how long. There are two men in the cabin—blast-burned. Their lock bin had been burned open, and this was caught in its door." He put the stone on a shelf. "And this is the ident card from the control slot." He laid the strip of metal next to the stone.

If he had planned to carry war into the enemy's territory, he succeeded for a space, for Meshler was staring from him to the two exhibits and then back again.

"We have also to report"—Ali broke the short silence—"unless Shannon has already done it for us, the presence of a mutated antline—"

Meshler finally came to life. He was closed-face now, all signs of surprise gone.

"It would seem"—his voice was as frosty as the air outside—"that you have been making a great many strange discoveries—very strange discoveries." He spoke, Dane thought, as if he considered most not only improbable but also impossible, but at least they had proof, good solid proof of it all.

8. INVOLUNTARY FLIGHT

"What is the situation, sir?" Having done his best to throw the opposition off balance, disregarding the last comment from the ranger, Dane turned to Tau. He wanted to know just what they had to face.

It was Meshler who answered. "You are all under arrest!" He said that weightedly, as if the words disarmed them and made the odds of four to one wholly in favor of that one. "I am to escort you to Trewsport, where your case comes under Patrol surveillance—"

"And the charge?" Kamil had not moved from the hatch door. His one arm was behind him, and Dane thought he still had a hand on the latch. It was plain that Ali did not consider the odds in Meshler's favor.

"Sabotage of shipment, interference with the mail, murder—" The ranger stated each charge as if he were a judge pronouncing sentence.

"Murder?" Ali looked surprised. "Whom did we murder?"

"Person unknown," Tau drawled. His former rigidity had eased. He leaned against the wall, one hand on the edge of the hammock where the brachs sat in their nest of padding. "You met him dead." He nodded to Dane. "He was wearing your face at the time—"

Now Meshler turned a sharp, measuring look at Dane, who, to aid him in identification, pushed back his hood. And for the second time the Terran saw a trace of surprise on the rather flat face of the ranger. Tau uttered a sound not far from a laugh.

"You see, Ranger Meshler, that our tale was the truth.

And the rest we can prove, as well as showing you a man with the same features as that mask. We have the box that caused all the trouble, the mutated embryos, the brachs— Let your science techs test it all, and they will see we reported nothing but the truth."

There was a wriggling against Dane's shoulders. He had forgotten the brach in the pack. Now he loosened the straps and held the bag so that its occupant could climb out to join his family in the hammock. Meshler viewed that without comment.

Now the ranger produced a tridee shot from an inner pocket. Holding it, he moved closer to the hammock that held the "people" from Xecho, looking from the picture of the brachs and back again several times.

"There are differences," he commented.

"As we told you. You heard them, or rather her, talk," Rip replied. There was a tightness in his voice that suggested the time before Ali and Dane's arrival had not been pleasantly spent.

"And where is this mysterious box?" The ranger did not look to them but continued to study the brachs. He gave the impression of still being skeptical.

"We buried it, in its protective covering," Dane replied. "Only it may not be the first such shipment to arrive here."

Now he did have the full attention of Meshler. Those chill chips of ice that served the other for eyes fastened on him. "You have reason for believing so?"

Dane told him of the antline. Whether he was making any impression on Meshler, he could not tell, but at least the man listened without any outward sign of incredulity.

"You found its lair, you say? And it was under stunner influence when you last saw it?"

"We backtracked it to the lair." Ali cut in. "And, from the marks, it was on its way back there when it left the cage. We didn't trail it again."

"No, you were after your other monsters, to cover up what you had introduced here." Meshler had not softened. "And these monsters—where are they now?"

"We tracked them as far as the river," Ali continued. "The brach said they had flown across, and we were hunting a way of getting over when we were recalled."

Tau spoke then. "The brach said? How did it know?"

"He"—Dane unconsciously corrected the pronoun—"says they can sense emotions. That's what led to the dragons' escape in the first place. One of the brach kits 'heard' their anger at being shut up in the cage and went to open that. They turned on the kit and then got away—"

He half expected the ranger to contradict that with scorn, but the man did not. He listened impassively, glancing now and then at the brachs.

"So we have a couple of monsters loose, besides this ant-line—"

"As well as two murdered men," Dane broke in, "who were dead long before we planeted."

"If they have been dead as long as you say," the ranger replied, "they can await attention for a short space longer. What we have to deal with firstly are these 'dragons' of yours." He put away the tridee and brought out a tube, which, at a slight squeeze, rolled out a map. Though it was in miniature, its points of references were so clearly marked it was easy to read.

"The lake." Meshler pointed. "Your river drains from there?"

"We believe so," Dane answered.

"And your dragons crossed it?" Slightly beyond the river line were marks of pale green. The ranger tapped those with fingertip.

"Cartl's holding. If your dragons headed for that—" Another pinch of finger and the map snapped back into the tube. "It would be better that we locate them before they get that far. This—this creature can track them? You are sure of that?"

"He says he can. He took us to the river." Dane moved; he had no intention of allowing the ranger to take the brach. After all, no matter what change had occurred, the alien was still part of the cargo for which Dane was responsible. But Meshler had not reached for the brach.

"You are under arrest." He looked around, catching them one by one with his straight stare, as if challenging them to deny his authority. "If we wait for a search party from Trewsport, it may be too late. I have my duty. If Cartl's holding is in danger, my first duty is there. But you loosed this danger; therefore, you have a duty also—"

"We have not denied that," Tau returned. "We have done

79

the best we could to insure that the port was not infected."

"The best you could? With these dragons loose to attack a holding?"

"What I can't understand," Dane said slowly, his words aimed at Tau, "is how they can withstand the cold. They were let out in the very early morning. I expected to find them frozen. Reptiles cannot take cold—"

"Lathsmers"—Meshler corrected—"are not reptiles. And they are well adapted to cold. They are acclimated for Trewsworld winters before they are decanted at hatching."

"But I tell you," Dane said angrily, "these are not your lathsmers—but probably the million-year-back ancestors of them. They are certainly reptiles to look at!"

"We can't know just what they are"—Tau corrected him—"until we have a chance to run them through a diagnostic lab. Their immunity to cold might well be a part of their conditioning the ray did not affect."

"We have no time to argue about their nature!" Meshler stated firmly. "We hunt and find them, before they cause more trouble. First I beam in my report. You stay here."

He shouldered past Ali and went out the hatch, slamming it behind him. Kamil spoke to Tau.

"What *is* going on?"

"We would all like to know a few details," Tau answered wearily. "When we landed, there was already information out—we had come in under suspicious circumstances. Then, we had to report a death on board—"

"But how?" began Shannon.

"Just so, how?" Tau returned. "We had not had time to report. We answered with the truth, showed them the body. I gave the port doctor my conclusions. They wanted his papers. When we told them he carried yours and showed them that mask, they were, or pretended to be, incredulous. Said they didn't think any such switch could be pulled without our knowing, that an imposture could not be maintained throughout the voyage, which is probably true. That being so, they logically went on to a new point, what would bring a man to stow away."

"So you told them about the box," Ali supplied.

"We had to at that point, since the lab people were yammering all over the place for their brachs—as well as the settlers for the embryos. We could have said one shipment was coming later but not both under the circumstances. Jellico has demanded a Board of Trade hearing. In the meantime, the *Queen* is impounded and the rest of the crew in custody. They sent this Meshler out to pick you up—with me to handle the brachs, since by trade law they have to have a medical officer for a live cargo."

"I-S behind this, you think?" Rip demanded.

"I don't believe so. There is still the problem of a big company doing a complicated plan to make trouble for one free trader. And it is not that we nudged them out of this mail contract. It had been Combine property for years. No, I think we were just handy, and someone used us. Maybe the same thing might have happened to a Combine ship if it were still on mail run."

"Craig"—Dane had been only half listening, his thoughts turning in another direction—"that dead man, could they have meant him to die? Was he expendable and that was why they didn't care if he lived long enough to be taken for a stowaway?"

"Could be true. Only why—?"

"And why, and why, and why?" Rip threw up his hands in a gesture of scattering unanswerable questions to the four points of the compass.

But Ali had picked up the stone Dane had brought from the wrecked crawler. He turned it around, studying it.

"Trewsworld is strictly an Ag planet, isn't it? Agriculture the only occupation?"

"That's been its rating."

"But dead prospectors in the bush, with a lock bin broken open? Where was this exactly?" Ali shot that question abruptly at Dane.

"Caught in under the melted door. I thought someone had swept out the contents in a big hurry and overlooked this sliver when it wedged fast."

Rip looked over Ali's shoulder at the stone. "Looks like ordinary rock to me."

"Ah, but you aren't a mineralogist, nor are any of us." Ali weighed the rock in his hand. "I have a distinct feeling that somehow an answer to all of this is hovering right under our noses, but we are just a little too dense to grasp its importance."

He was still holding the rock when the hatch creaked open and Meshler was again with them.

"You"—he pointed to Shannon—"stay here. There will be a guard ship from the port to pick you up. And you, also." This time his pointing finger singled out Ali. "But you and you, and this—this creature you say can sniff out the dragons of yours—will come with me. We take the flitter and pick up those things and do it quickly!"

For a moment it seemed that Shannon and Kamil might protest, but Dane saw them look to Tau, and though there was no change of expression on the medic's face, Dane believed they had received some message not to interfere with Meshler's arrangements.

For the second time Dane fitted the brach into the pack, the alien making no protest, as if he had been able to follow their conversation and knew the purpose of this second expedition. And neither did the ranger demand Dane turn over his stunner before they went out to the flitter.

"We go first to Cartl's," Meshler announced in his authoritative voice. He motioned Dane to the side seat by his own at the controls, the Terran settling the brach's pack on his lap, while Tau had one of the rear seats.

Whatever else he might be, the ranger was an expert pilot. Perhaps flitter flight was the normal travel for one representing the law in this wide territory. He brought them up effortlessly, swung the nose of the craft to the southeast, and pushed the speed to high.

It seemed only seconds until they flashed over the river. Then there were billows of the fat-leaved trees under them again, almost as if the forest were another kind of water. The brach sat quietly on Dane's lap, its head thrust well out of the coverings. The cabin was warm enough so none of them pulled up their hoods, and as that horned nose swung back and forth a little, Dane could almost believe that it quested for some scent.

Suddenly it pointed to the right, more to the westward than their present line of flight. The brach's voice echoed thinly in the mike of Dane's hood.

"Dragons, there—"

Meshler, startled, turned his attention from the controls. The brach's nose continued to point as if registering to some signal.

"How do you know?" the ranger demanded.

Dane repeated his question for translation.

"Dragons hungry, follow meat—"

Hunting! Well, hunger certainly had an emotional side, and it could be very sharp in a feral creature. But Meshler did the flying. Would he allow them to be hunters in turn, or would he insist upon keeping to his original course? Before Dane could urge the hunt on him, the ranger turned, and the brach's nose, as if it were indeed an indicator geared to the controls, now pointed directly ahead.

"Holding," Meshler informed them. Scattered among the stumps were odd enclosures of poles, not set tightly together to form fences but placed at even distances, apparently to support rungs or rails. And in the light of the afternoon, they could see that most of those had a living burden which pushed, jostled, and shot out long necks to peck at companions crowding too close. Lathsmers!

"They let them run loose—no guards?" wondered Dane, remembering the antline—and perhaps Trewsworld had native predators, too.

Meshler made a sound that might pass for a laugh.

"They have their own defenses. Now even a man comes in such fields without a stunner. Though if you go in in a crawler and take it slow, they don't seem to notice. There aren't many things big or tough enough to take on a covey of lathsmers."

The brach on Dane's lap screeched, not any intelligible word, as they flew on, out over a battlefield where a bloody melee was still in progress.

The roosting rails of the lathsmers at this point were fewer than in the first field, and they were clear of the birds. There were some battered bodies ripped and limp on the ground. But two of the rightful inhabitants of the roost were still on their feet, shooting out heads, naked of feathers, murderous beaks spear-pointed at their enemies.

Those were—Dane could not at first believe what his eyes reported. The embryos that had hatched had been then about the size of the female brach. These things were a little larger than the lathsmers. Their quick attacks, feints, use of talons, lashing tails, battering wings on which they could raise high enough to threaten the lathsmers from above, could have all belonged to adults fully matured and seasoned by many such forays.

"They—they've grown!" His amazement made him state the obvious. He still could not believe that a single day or two days could have produced such alteration.

"Those your dragons? And you expect me to believe them just decanted?" Meshler was incredulous, as well he might be. But they were the same things Rip, Ali, and Dane had installed in the cage—in miniature then.

"They are."

Meshler brought the flitter around, for they had swept well over the site of the savage struggle. They swooped down. Dane believed the ranger was trying to frighten the dragons away from the remaining lathsmers. He had his own stunner ready. They would have to come within closer range before he could use it. Meshler fumbled with one hand in the front of his tunic. Now he held out to Dane an egg-shaped ball.

"Push in the top pin," he ordered. "Drop it as close to them as you can when we go over again."

Once more they had skimmed away from the battle. Dane opened the window to his right, moving the brach down between his knees for safekeeping, and leaned out ready to drop the ovoid.

Meshler was taking them even closer to the ground on his third pass. Dane only hoped he could judge distance. His thumb sent the plunger even with the surface of the ball, and he let it go. The ranger must have gunned the flitter, for their forward sweep was at such a sudden excess of speed as to pin Dane against the seat, but as they went, the speed decreased, and when the craft turned once more, they had fallen to a landing rate.

Landing here among the stumps on rough terrain where brush had been grubbed out without regard for soothing was going to take maneuvering. They headed once more for the broken roost. But now around those splintered poles curled greenish vapor, which whirled before it broke into thin wisps and rose up and up to disappear well above the height at which they now flew.

Of the creatures that had, only moments earlier, been engaged in ruthless war, there was nothing to be seen, unless they had joined the bodies on the ground. Meshler set down in the only possible open space, still some distance from the raided roost.

Dane left the brach in the flitter, running with Meshler and Tau toward the scene of the struggle. If the dragons had come originally to hunt for food, perhaps the resistance of the lathsmers had sealed the fate of the whole covey. Or else it was not mere wanton killing on the dragons' part but defense against the fighting prowess of creatures they had underestimated.

The dragons and the last two of the lathsmers were lying as they had fallen, but they were not dead. The discharge of the vapor had had much the same effect as that of a stunner beam. Meshler stood over the mutants, studying them.

"You say these are the ancestors of the lathsmers?" He sounded unconvinced, and had Dane not seen them crawl from the embryo containers, he would have been as hard to satisfy.

"Unless they were shipped wrongly," Tau commented. "But I think you can forget that. These were snoop-rayed at the port of Xecho—routine—but the field experts don't miss anything."

Meshler stooped, lifted the edge of a wing, which was ribbed with rubbery skin spreading between the ribs, then allowed it to fall back against the scaled body, where snorting breaths expanded and contracted wrinkled, repulsive skin.

"If your trick box can do this—"

"Not *our* box," Dane corrected. "And remember the antline—that box is probably not the first of its kind."

"Report!" Meshler spoke as if to himself. "Now—" He brought a tangler from his belt, a weapon meant to render any prisoner completely immobile. He used it with expert care, leaving each of the dragons well encased, limbs, tail, wings, and cruelly toothed jaws.

They dragged them back to the flitter, loading them into the cargo section. Meshler shook his head over the remains of the lathsmers. The two who had fought to the last, he thought would survive. But the rest were dead. To report this to the unfortunate owner must be their next move.

"He'll claim damages," Meshler commented with satisfaction. And if he wants to swear land-hurt against you all—"

Dane did not know what land-hurt might be, but from the ranger's tone it was more trouble for the *Queen.*

"Not our doing," Tau answered.

"No? Your cargo was not officially discharged at the port —this part of it wasn't—so you are still responsible for it. And if a cargo damages—"

A nice legal point, Dane thought. They were responsible certainly for damge to a cargo, but could they be held also for damage *by* a cargo? He thought feverishly of all the instruction tapes he had studied, both during his years of schooling and after he had joined the *Queen*. Had such a case of this kind ever come up before? He could not recall it. Van Ryke would know, but Van Ryke was parsecs away— in another galactic sector—and the Spirit of Outer Space only knew when he was going to planet to join them.

"Take the shortest way." Again Meshler appeared to be talking to himself. But a few minutes later, instead of turning east as his course had been earlier, the nose of the small craft veered west.

Meshler gave an exclamation and thumped a fist against one of the dials on the board. Its needle quivered a fraction but did not turn. Then he went to work, snapping levers, pushing buttons. There was no answering alteration in their course.

"What's the matter?" Dane was enough of a flitter pilot himself to know that the craft was now acting as if it were locked on automatics, on a set course, and that the ranger could not break to hand control.

Tau leaned forward, his head nearly even with Dane's. "Look at that indicator! We're on a control beam!"

One of the dials did read that they were riding a powerful and pulling beam.

"I can't break it!" Meshler's hands dropped from the board. "It won't answer the manuals."

"But if no one set a course—and they didn't—" Dane stared at the dial. Automatics could be set, even locked securely. But none of them had done that, and though they had been engrossed in getting the dragons on board, no one could have approached the flitter without being seen.

"Contact beam," Meshler said thoughtfully, "but that is impossible! There is nothing in this direction. Oh, a few wandering hunters, maybe. And the Trosti experimental station. But that's well north of here. And even they do not have the equipment to—"

"Somebody has," Tau said. "And it would seem your wilderness holds more than you supposed, Ranger Meshler. How closely do you patrol it, anyway?"

Meshler's head came up. There was a flush on his cheeks.

"We face now half a continent of wilderness. Most of it was aerial mapped. But as for exploring on land, we have too few men, very meager funds. And our jobs are to patrol and protect the holdings. There's never been any trouble on Trewsworld before—"

"If you are going to say before the *Queen* arrived," Dane retorted bitterly, "don't. We didn't produce a retrogressed antline, nor murder those two men in the crawler. And we certainly didn't entangle our own ship on purpose. If we are caught in a contact beam, it has to be broadcast from an installation. So there's more in the wilderness than you know."

But Meshler did not seem to be listening. Instead, the ranger activated the com, holding the mike in his hand and rattling off a series of letters that must have been in code. Three times he repeated that, waiting each time for a reply. Then, as nothing came, he hung the mike back on its hook with a small shrug of his shoulders.

"Com out, too?" Tau asked.

"It would seem so," Meshler answered. And still the flitter bored into a coming dusk of twilight, heading west into what the ranger admitted was the unknown.

9. HUNTERS OF MEN

The dark closed in, but when Dane would have snapped on the lights of the flitter, as Meshler made no move to, the ranger caught his wrist.

"No use letting ourselves be seen," he explained, and Dane was disconcerted at his own instinctive but perhaps dangerous move.

"Where are we? Any clue?" Tau asked.

"Southwest! To our reports there is nothing here but the wilds," Meshler returned. "Have I not said that?"

"This Trosti station," persisted the medic. "With what are their experiments concerned? Ag work, veterinary procedures, or general research?"

"Ag work, but not altogether for Trewsworld. They have a conditioning-for-export license. But they are of no concern. I have visited them on my rounds. We are well past that site, plus the fact that they had no installation capable of a beam such as this."

"Trosti," Tau repeated thoughtfully. "Trosti—"

"Vegan Trosti. This is one of the foundations set up under his will," Meshler supplied.

Vegan Trosti! Dane thought of the hundreds of rumors and supposedly authentic stories about Vegan Trosti. He was one of those men possessing what Terrans used to claim was a "golden touch." Every invention he backed, every exploration he financed, was a success, pouring more and more credits into his hoard. No one had ever learned just how much wealth Trosti had amassed. At intervals he made over some astronomical sum to a research project. If that paid off, and they regularly did, the profit went to the lucky planet giving it a base.

There were, of course, the other tales, too, such as grew from the shadow of such a man—that his "luck" was not always a matter for open investigation; that some of the research projects could not bear too open a scrutiny, or that they carried on programs on two levels, one that could be reviewed openly, the other masked by the first and for purposes far less advantageous for the public.

But, though such rumors had become legends also, there had never been one bit of proof they were true. And the credit side of Trosti's ledger was very impressive. If he had made any mistakes or taken any steps along another road, such were buried and forgotten.

So had Vegan Trosti lived, a power about whose person practically nothing was known. He shunned publicity with an almost fierce hatred. There were stories that he often worked among his own employees—especially on explorations—without their knowing it. When he disappeared, he had set up such a tight legal control of his empire, insuring that it was to be used for knowledge and general good, that he was looked upon on many worlds as a hero, almost a demigod.

How he had disappeared was not known, in spite of the investigation of the Patrol. It seemed that his deputies simply came forward some planet years back and announced that his private ship was long overdue and that they had their instructions in such a case to dissolve his holdings, carrying out his express commands. They had proceeded to do so, in spite of a bright beam of publicity allowing no concealment.

The story was that he had set off on one of his expeditions and that he had ceased to report regularly as he had always done. Following the time order he had left, his men moved to do as he wished should such a circumstance arrive.

Never had anyone learned anything about his early years. His past, beyond a certain point, was as blank as his final ending. He was a comet that had shot across the inhabited galaxy and left changes on those worlds it touched.

"We're losing altitude," Meshler suddenly exclaimed.

"Something else—" Once more Tau leaned forward so that his head and shoulders were close to the two before him. "See here?" His arm was a dark shadow in the dusky cabin, but what he held out for them had its own light about a dial. On the face of that, a needle quivered to the right, and from it came a buzzing, which seemed to Dane to grow even stronger.

"What—?" began Meshler.

"There is radiation ahead, radiation of the same type but stronger than that from the box on the *Queen*. I think we are going to have some answers to questions shortly."

"Listen—" Dane could not see the ranger's face. It was only a lightish blur in the gloom, but there was a note in the other's voice he had not heard before. "You say this radiation turns a thing back through time, retrogresses it—"

"All we have is the evidence of the embryos and the brach," Tau said.

"Well, suppose it affected us. Could it?"

"I don't know. That box was brought on board the ship by a human. Thorson saw it being handled by an alien woman. Of course, they may have sent their messenger on board to die, but I don't think so. They needed the *Queen* to ferry their cargo here, and the ship could not have been handled by a crew who retrogressed as rapidly as the animals it affected. We would not have been able to come out of hyper. But if the radiation is stepped up, then I am not sure—"

"And you say that's the same radiation ahead?"

"By the reading on this, yes."

But what he might have added to that was never said, for the flitter gave a sudden downward swoop. Meshler cried out and wrestled with the controls—to no purpose. He could not wrench the craft from the force pulling it earthward.

"Crash aid!" Dane sensed rather than saw the pilot's hand swing out to hit the panic button. He did the same on his side of the cabin. How much time did they have? Enough? The ground was only a dark mass, and he had no idea of how fast they were falling to meet it.

He felt the soft spurt of safe-foam on his body, curdling around it in the protective device of the flitter. It twined and coiled as he sat. Now it was as high as his throat, about his chin. He followed crash procedure, settled back in his seat, and shut his eyes as the protective covering jellied in around the three of them and the brach. Dane should have warned the brach, but he had forgotten all about the creature, who had been so quiet, and now it was too late.

Relax. His mind fought his nerves. Relax, leave it to the protective jelly. Tense up and he would delay the safety factor in that. Relax. He set his will to that now.

They struck. In spite of the safe-foam, it was a jar that knocked Dane into semiconsciousness. He did not know how long it was before he regained his senses enough to grope for the release catch on the cabin door to his right. He had to fight the pressure of the jelly to do that, but at last his fingers closed on the bar, but his half hold was torn loose as the door was opened with a sharp jerk. The jellied foam slipped toward that opening, carrying him with it as he struggled feebly to break free.

The safe-foam was being torn away. A great scarf of it fell from his head and shoulders. He opened his eyes into a blinding glare of beamer and blinked, unable to see, nor as yet able to understand what had happened. They had crashed and then—

Hands pulled him free of the foam with no care or gentleness. Speed seemed to be the thing desired. When he could stand, he was jerked to his feet, the beamer still so centered on him that he could not see who held it or the faces of the men who stripped off the jelly. There were two of them, and when they had done, they swung him expertly around and applied a tangler to his arms and wrists behind his back. Now he was as safely their prisoner as if they had encased him from shoulder to waist in plasta of the quick-drying sort.

Having made sure of him, they gave a shove that sent him staggering forward until he bumped against a surface with painful force. With that to steady him, he edged around. The bedazzlement left by the beam straight in his eyes was wearing off. He could see, though the men who were working on Tau remained only shadowy figures.

Dane never knew how many of them there were, for he was sure some of the party kept out of sight, using the beamer as a cover, but they worked with such efficiency that one could believe this was an action in which they had been drilled.

They had all three from the flitter under control. But they had not brought out the pack with the brach! Didn't they know about the animal, or didn't they consider the alien important?

The jelly, once exposed to the air, would disappear as the strips pulled from the prisoners were already doing, so that the brach would be freed shortly by himself. But the alien might be so terrorized by the crash and the jellied foam that—Dane did not know what he expected of—or for—the brach. Then he heard the crashing of what could only be a crawler in progress toward them, and he hoped the alien would escape notice.

A line snaked out of the dark into the path of the beamer, was hooked fast to the fore of the flitter, and that mass of wreckage began to move, complainingly, under the steady pull of the crawler. Dane was not to see its eventual destination. A hand caught his shoulder, dragged him away from his support, but continued to push him along over a very rough path, where he stumbled and would have gone down several times if the unseen guard and guide had not kept his hold.

They came at last into a clearing, where a rock ledge jutted out to make a roof over a camp. There was a portable cooker there and other gear piled under the overhang, enough to suggest their captors had been there for some time and were well equipped.

There was also a diffuse lamp, which gave a subdued light. It had been set on lowest level, as if the campers begrudged the need for it at all.

In that glow Dane was able to see the three men who had brought them in. They wore regulation one-piece hunting suits with the instrument- and tool-hung belts of those venturing into the wild on a planet not native to them. All three were Terran or Terran colonial stock. But the one who rose from beside the lamp at their coming was not.

He was of a species strange to Dane, very tall, so that he had to hunch his shoulders and incline his head under that roofing ledge. In the light his skin was yellow (not brown-yellow, as one of ancient Terran Oriental stock might be, but a brighter hue). And his eyes and his teeth as he opened his mouth gave off fluorescence—the eyes being ringed with some glowing substance.

His hair was scant and grew in ring patches, with even spaces between, about a skull that rose to a cone-dome at the top. But his body, save that his arms and legs appeared too long for the size of his torso, was like that of a Terran and covered also by a hunter's suit.

Dane wondered if Tau, with his greater knowledge of X-Tees, could name the species. From whatever world he came, it was plain that the alien was in command of the camp. He did not speak but gestured, and the three from the flitter were shoved on, back against the rock wall, then pushed down, to sit facing out into the night, while the tall alien hunkered down beside the lamp. What he held in his hands, curiously limber hands—his fingers moved as if they were boneless tentacles—was a com. But he did not speak into it. Instead, he used the tips of two of those squirming fingers to beat against the mike in a swift clicking.

None of the men spoke to the prisoners, nor did Meshler ask questions. When Dane glanced at the ranger, he saw that the man was studying the scene with an intentness that suggested he was making a mental listing.

The strangers wore hunters' clothing. Their equipment was that Dane had seen used by sport hunters on other worlds. But if they had legitimately entered the wilderness on Trewsworld with that excuse, they would have been licensed and had with them a guide. There was no sign of any guide. Nor did they hear again the crawler that had dragged away the flitter. Dane deduced that the party was larger, and there might be a reason for the others to keep out of sight.

Having sent his click message, the tall alien brought out a long, hooded cloak, wrapping it well about him, and went to curl up at the other end of the camp under the ledge. He was followed shortly afterward, not to the same place, but into slumber, by two of the three Terrans, none of whom had so much as glanced at their prisoners since they had herded them in. The third man remained by the fire and held an unholstered tangler across his knee.

Dane knew little of electronics, but in this camp he saw nothing like the box from the *Queen*. Nor was there anything to suggest that the powerful force that had brought down the flitter had its source here. The puzzle that had enmeshed the *Queen* gave hope of clue now and then, but none such led anywhere.

He was tired, but in his present uncomfortable position he was not so fatigued that sleep came. Nor, when he looked at Tau and Meshler, had they succumbed either. The sentry by the fire now and then arose to walk back and forth, dividing his attention between a quick glance at the captives and a longer look into the dark beyond the very limited light of the lamp.

He was on one such beat when Dane caught a flicker at the other end of the campsite. Something moved there, and with caution. It was far too small for even a creeping man. The brach! Though why he expected the alien to have tracked them here, Dane could not say. The creature would be more likely to run away from the threat of a party who had so easily taken men prisoners.

The sentry turned, and now Dane could see nothing at all. When the man came back to the lamp, Dane was not quite sure he had ever seen anything.

Yet he kept stealing glances in that direction, being careful not to turn his head, to attract in any way the attention of the sentry. And he was rewarded seconds later by the sign of another flitting, this time from the protection of brush to a second cover behind a couple of supply boxes. There was no mistaking that silhouette—the long horned snout of the brach.

What the alien proposed to do (unless he had merely followed to cling to the proximity of the three from the flitter because their familiarity was a forlorn feeling of security), Dane could not guess. He had seen the brach use a stunner. But those who had stripped them out of the safe-foam had disarmed them. And, unless there had been some weapons in the flitter that the brach had located, he had no chance if discovered. There was no way of communication possible, yet Dane found himself thinking a warning over and over—not that that would carry.

The sentry got up for another of those periodic prowls, and as he turned his back, the brach scuttled out into the open, as soundless in his passing as if he were a shadow. Making a quick dash, the alien was now crouched beside Tau, his head stretched at an uncomfortable angle. The horn—he was using his horn on the cords of the tangle!

Being what they were, those spun restrainers could not be easily cut or broken. They were ultra elastic on the surface, yielding under pressure of knife blade but not allowing their thick surfaces to be cut.

Yet Dane could see the small movements of the brach's head. He must be tearing at those ties. Tau winced as if those efforts were painful, but he did not move and held steady.

Then Tau's arms flexed a fraction, and Dane knew a spurt of excitement. Somehow the brach had broken the tangle strand. Tau was free, though he made no move to act upon that freedom.

However, the medic leaned forward slowly, holding his body as far as he could away from the wall, and Dane knew that the brach was wriggling through to come to Dane's own assistance. He was right, for shortly thereafter he felt the fluffy warmth of the creature pressed tightly to him, the jerk and tug on the tangle as the alien sawed away with the horn. Then, too, he was freed, edging away from the wall, in turn, to give the brach a chance to reach Meshler.

The guard had completed his sentry beat and settled down again by the lamp, though he continued to divide his watch between the prisoners and the outer dark. He was too alert for unarmed men to make any plan not well thought out.

At last he got to his feet and went to one of his sleeping comrades to shake him awake. Oddly enough the roughly aroused man said nothing, only accepted the tangler and the post by the lamp, while the first rolled up in the same coverings from which the other had just crawled. Their silence struck an odd note—it was almost as if they could not talk.

The brach had wriggled from behind Meshler, and Dane knew that the ranger must also be free. The alien worked his way along, using the men and shadows for cover, finally hunkering down behind the pile of boxes that had been his first goal upon entering the camp. The guard by the lamp was on sentry go now. Just as he reached the most outward point of his beat, the brach moved. Dane could not quite make out what the creature had loosened and pushed, but it rolled with a clatter for the lamp. In the last few seconds before it struck, Dane made ready.

It had impact enough to overbalance the lamp, and the light went out. Dane and the others threw themselves forward, out of range, or so they hoped, of any tangle discharge. Nor did Dane try to get to his feet, but scuttled, keeping as belly-down as he could, heading for the open. Sounds told him that his companions must be following the same tactics.

He expected to hear a shout from the sentry, some outcry to awaken the sleepers. There was a scuffling, and he heard the hiss of what could only be a tangler discharged. But if that touched anyone, it was not him.

Then he was out, getting to his feet. He brushed against another body, flailed out with his arm, and felt the slick surface of a thermo jacket. A hand caught his, linked fingers, and together they made what speed they could into the thick brush lying to the right of the ledge. That vegetation would deflect any tangler. But surely their captors had more dangerous weapons—

"Tau?"

"Yes!" The whisper was from his side.

"Meshler?"

"I don't know," the medic whispered.

They had no way of keeping their forced entry into the brush silent. The crackle of their passing must be a loud

95

announcement of their path to their late captors. Then Dane was brought up short as a pair of hands seized him, and he swung about, aiming a blind blow at his assailant.

"Quiet!" There was no mistaking the ranger's voice. "Take it smooth—easy!"

He tugged Dane along, and Dane's own hold on the medic drew him in turn. The ranger certainly had, Dane decided, an extraordinary degree of night sight, for they were no longer threshing about in brush, though that did beat at them as they threaded a way along, either following a winding path or going through a thinner area of growth.

Their best pace was not a good one. Dane still wondered why there had been no sounds of alarm from the camp. Then came a sudden spring of light. The diffuse lamp must not only be working again but also turned higher. Only the fugitives were screened by the growth in between.

The plates in their space boots clicked on a more solid surface, and the brush was gone. Walls of some kind rose dark and solid on either hand. Dane looked up. He could see a narrow strip with a star or two emblazoned in it.

Something brushed his knee. He broke his hold on his two companions and stooped to feel the brach. The alien was shivering, and Dane held him close while he unsealed the seal of his thermo jacket and pulled it around them both.

"What is it?" whispered Meshler.

"The brach—he's cold." Dane wondered how long the creature had suffered the cruel night air.

"Does it—he—know where the flitter is?" Meshler's whisper was urgent.

In handling the brach, Dane had discovered the alien still wore the translator. Now he pulled at his hood and whispered into the mike, "The flying thing—where is it?"

"In a hole—in the ground." To his relief the alien answered promptly. Dane had thought that he might be half conscious from cold.

"Where?"

The brach wriggled in his hold and Dane felt his head bump against his chin as it turned, pointing left.

"Left—in a hole, he says," Dane reported to the ranger. Meshler started so confidently in that direction that it was as if he could see clearly. But when the Terrans stumbled and lagged, he came back.

"Hurry!"

"Do us no good to hurry if we get broken bones for it," Tau returned reasonably.

"But," Meshler began, "this is open ground."

"In the dark," countered Tau, "it could be anything."

"Dark? You mean you can't *see?*" Meshler sounded honestly surprised, almost shocked.

"Not at night, not well enough to go charging along through this," Tau answered.

"I did not know. Wait then!" Meshler's indistinct figure twisted about. Then the end of a belt flapped into Dane's reach. "Link together—I'll lead."

As soon as Dane caught the belt and Tau's hand was set on his shoulder, the ranger stepped out as confidently as if he held a beamer focused on the path ahead.

"Still this way?" he asked a moment later.

"This way?" Dane relayed through the translator to the brach.

"It is so. Soon big hole—"

Dane supplied that information. And soon indeed did they come to a big hole—a break from the height on which they stood, leading to an unknown dark plunge.

"You see anything?" he asked.

"They've finished off the flitter," Meshler returned bleakly. "But we'll need supplies—if they've left any."

The belt was suddenly hanging limp and loose in Dane's grasp, and he heard sounds that must mean that Meshler was descending to the flitter.

10. THE TRAP

This was no time to stop to explore wreckage, Dane protested silently. With that lamp blazing behind, the hunt must be up. And who piloted the crawler that had dragged the flitter here? Those extra members of the enemy party might well be closing in on them now!

He remembered the brach's ability to trace by reading emotions. Surely that cast off by a hunting party would be strong enough for the alien to detect.

"Do others come?" he murmured into the translator. Dane felt the brach shift its position against him and knew that the alien was turning his head as if the long nose were the pickup of some super radar.

"Behind, not elsewhere—"

Rocket blast and beam burn Meshler! They had to get out of here, and the ranger had left them more or less trapped while he went nosing around the useless wreck. It was a fact—it must be—that those who had taken them captive would not have left weapons down there. Or would they? Suppose they were trying to make the whole mess seem an accidental wreck. Then surely they would not have looted it. But a wreck needed bodies—

A chill threaded along Dane's spine. Bodies had been to hand, ready for when they were needed to complete that cover-up. Perhaps they had wanted information first, before they were ready to turn live captives into dead bodies. And the longer the three lingered here—the four, Dane reminded himself (for the brach had proved so far the most useful member of their party)—the more certain it was that the plan on the part of the enemy might just be successful.

"We've got to get out of here!" He stated the obvious to Tau. "What's the use of his prowling around down there? They'll catch up with us soon."

"Do you want to try it on your own?" queried the medic. "It's apparent Meshler has night sight to a surprising degree. Unless those jacks share it, he can cut a trail they can follow only slowly."

"Jacks?" Dane caught the one word that should not have surprised him as much as it momentarily did, for this was plainly an illegal group operating under cover, though jacks did not usually go in for elaborate planning. Strike and get away was their general pattern.

"What would they want here?"

"Who knows? Maybe Meshler does, or he ought to. Listen!"

They froze. Dane felt the medic tense as they stood, shoul-

98

der touching shoulder. That sound did not come from behind; it was from below. Meshler climbing up? Dane hoped fervently that was true.

"Let us go." Meshler's voice sounded from almost at Dane's feet. The Terran started back and felt the belt jerk and tauten in his hand. And then, towed as he had been before, Tau's hand on his shoulder, Dane followed the ranger. At intervals, Meshler whispered some terse direction to follow, but he did not say what he had found at the wreck, though a bundle slung over his shoulder now and again bumped against the hand with which Dane held the belt.

They made better time than Dane had hoped, though he was so confused by the dark that he could not have told in which direction they were now headed. If they were on their way back to the grounded LB, there must be several days of tramping before them. So perhaps Meshler's search of the wreck for supplies was nessary.

Time meant nothing. At intervals Meshler halted to give them a breather. Dane and Tau took turns carrying the brach inside their jackets. The small alien no longer shivered but felt warm and relaxed when it was Dane's turn to assume his weight again, so the Terran hoped he had taken no ill from his period in the night's cold.

Dawn found them in a place of rocks, which were wind and erosion carved into weird and amazing shapes. Block masses of apparently great weight were supported on conical pillars. All of the large outcrops were riddled with holes and crevices, some almost the size of a small cave. It was an excellent place to take cover for longer than a breathing halt, and apparently Meshler selected it for that very reason.

Dane had not realized how tired he was until he hunkered down in the place the ranger chose, a niche between several rocks. Tramping in space boots was not an exercise he would recommend. While there was no more tough and sturdy footware to be found on any world, the weight of their magnetic sole plates made tired feet feel as if they had a massive bracelet of iron soldered about the ankles.

"Loosen the seals." Tau leaned forward to snap up those on his own as he spoke. "But don't take them off—not if you want to get them on again in a hurry."

Even the loosening of the tight seals gave a measure of relief that made Dane sigh. Meshler opened the bag he had

brought from the flitter. Now he drew from it a single ration tube. Dane could have squeezed all its contents into
his own mouth, but good sense told him that Meshler was
right as the ranger measured it in fours, carefully sucking
only the first quarter before he pased it to Tau. The medic
squeezed the second portion out on a rock, from which
the brach, shooting out a long, pale tongue, licked it in two
passes. And having taken his own part, Tau passed the
now almost flat tube to Dane, who finished it off as slowly
as possible, hoping to feel less hungry when it was down.

Of course, E ration was highly sustaining. A man could
keep going on a portion of a tube such as they had just
shared out. But it was like a taste of a dish when one
wanted to scoop the whole of its contents onto one's plate.

"We're heading north. How far back is it to the LB or to
that holding you spoke of?" Dane wanted to know when he
was sure there was no infinitesimal bit left in the tube.

"Too far—both—to make without transportation," was
Meshler's daunting reply. "We can't go on foot with very
limited rations and no weapons—"

"I thought you said there were no really dangerous animals," Dane argued. He dared not accept the ranger's dark
point of view.

"We are hunted men," Tau reminded him. "Very well,
if we can't strike north, what do we do?"

"The crawler—" Meshler fastened the bag. "Also, this—"
He held out something to Tau, and Dane recognized the
detect with which Tau had picked up the radiation when
they were helpless in the beam-controlled flitter.

"Does it still work?" the ranger asked.

Tau inspected it carefully and then pressed a button on
the top. Straightway the needle came to life and spun to
point directly at the man who held it.

"It works. Now, in which direction was that camp? I am
so turned around that I don't know north from south."

"There—" Meshler stabbed a finger to Tau's left with such
confidence that they had to believe him.

"Then the source of the radiation is not there."

"No equipment in sight," Dane observed.

"That box was compact. They could have had something
like it buried. But this says that direction—" The medic
motioned over his own shoulder.

"No way of telling how far away?" Meshler asked.

"No, except the beam is stronger."

The ranger leaned his head against the rock behind him. "We cannot make it on foot, even as far as Cartl's holding. And that is the southernmost outpost." He might have been thinking aloud as he imparted that gloomy information. "A crawler is slow and heavy, and it is not normally used far from a base camp, where it can be maintained."

"Those prospectors had a crawler," Dane broke in.

"They must also have had a camp," Meshler returned heavily. "And this one, under the ledge"—he came back to the present problem—"is a temporary one only. Therefore—"

"We head straight back into their hands?" flashed Dane. "Are you space-whirly, man?"

"I am ranger trained." Meshler showed no annoyance at Dane's impatience. "Those men in hunters' clothing—I do not think they were hunters."

"We have no weapons," Tau reminded him. "Or did you pick some up at the flitter?"

"No. It is my belief they would have been put back on us when we were returned to the scene. These men will be after us, yes, but they will expect us to head north. If we go south and get that crawler—or other transport—we have a chance. Otherwise—" He did not finish that sentence. His eyes closed, and Dane suddenly realized that the trip through the night must have been a double strain on the ranger playing eyes for three men.

"I take first watch?" Tau looked to Dane.

He wanted to say no, but he could not pull that denial out of the weight of fatigue that deadened his body. "First watch," he agreed, and as he settled back against the stone, much in Meshler's position, he was already half asleep.

When Tau aroused him for sentry duty, the pale winter sun was high overhead, and there was actually a mild sensation of warmth. By chance or design, Meshler had chosen their pocket stronghold well. It faced northwest—the direction from which they might logically expect their pursuers to come. And the only way anyone could get at them was up a narrow strip of open climb, steep enough so that a couple of well-placed boulders could be rolled down it. Only, such boulders did not exist nearby as Dane discovered when he crawled stiffly out of the half cave and stretched his arms and legs, though keeping in the shadow of the rocks.

Some flying things cruised the air, soaring and dropping on spread wings that flapped only once in a while, but those were clearly native to this land. At ground level nothing moved. Dane longed for a pair of distance lenses—they should have been in the flitter, but now they might as well be in one of the pockets on Trewsworld's well-cratered moon for all the good they did him.

Meshler's proposal to go on into the heart of what might be enemy territory apparently made sense to the ranger, but Dane was dubious. Now as he squatted at the entrance to their shelter, the brach crawled out from between Meshler and Tau, where he had been cradled in their warmth, and came to Dane, sitting up next to the Terran.

"Are there any below?" Dane said to the hood mike.

The long head turned in a slow swing right to left and back again.

"No one comes. Hunter there—" The alien indicated one of the wheeling winged dots. "It hungers, it waits—but not for us."

Dane had confidence in the brach's senses, but not enough to lead him to forsake his vantage point and watch on the land below.

"There have been—" the brach continued.

"Been what?" Dane prodded.

"Been men here."

"Here!" Dane was startled.

"Not in this place, below—there—" Again the brach pointed, downslope to the left.

"How do you know?"

"Machine smell." It seemed to Dane that long nose raised in a gesture of distaste. "Not now—but once."

"Stay here—watch," Dane told the brach. He could see no tracks of any machine. But if the crawler had passed this way, then it would have left some and a trail they could follow. Better than just striking off into the blue with Tau's detect as their only guide.

He took all precautions, working his way downslope, though, he thought with a wry grimace, doubtless to one of Meshler's training he probably made every mistake in the manual. When he reached the point to which the brach had

102

directed him, he discovered the alien was right. There were deep indentations of a crawler's tread—and on a rock a smear of oil, which must have alerted the sensitive nose of the alien.

Allowing for the twists of a passage made to take every advantage of any ease on the very rough ground here, the trail did run to the south, not quite in the same direction as Tau's detect, but enough so to suggest that end of trail and radiation had a common source. He traced it only a short distance, having no mind to be spotted by any jack traveler.

Dane was not long back in position at the opening of the shelter before Meshler roused. He moved out to join the Terran. Dane reported his discovery, only to see the ranger slink down with caution, returning shortly thereafter.

"Not a regular road," he said as he reached for the pack to bring out another ration tube. "The thing only went through there once, and it was in difficulties."

"The oil smear?" Dane asked.

"That—and one of the treads had a frayed edge. It might well have been heading in for repairs, taking a short-cut." He again measured off four sections on the tube, being meticulously just.

Having eaten his own portion, he squeezed out one for the brach before handing the tube to Dane. And the Terran, finishing his share, put the tube near Tau's hand for his awakening.

"Nothing else?" the ranger asked.

"No. He agrees to that." Dane indicated the brach, licking his muzzle with his long tongue.

"We go on, in the dark." Meshler lifted his head much as did the brach when sniffing. "Clear tonight—a fuller moon—"

Not that that would make much difference, thought Dane. Meshler might declare a night to be clear, as it probably was for him, while it remained dark to the Terrans.

It was late afternoon, and Dane had dozed off again when he was roused by Tau. Once more they shared a ration tube, and then Meshler signaled a move. The sun was half-way down behind some sawtoothed mountains, and already shadows were reaching out in dusky advance.

Relying on the brach's warning, Dane carried the alien within his jacket, though having to leave it unsealed to do so meant that some of the warmth was lost. They started out along the track left by the crawler. Before the light had entirely gone, they came across one place where the chewed-up soil suggested the machine had stalled, to be dug loose. The scuffed marks left by boots were too badly blurred to let them guess how many passengers the vehicle had carried.

The detect in Tau's hand continued to point in the same general direction. However, the medic reported that the amount of radiation was not mounting. It was the brach who about midnight or thereabouts gave them their warning.

"Things—" Its pipe sounded in Dane's hood mike. "Danger—"

"Men?" he asked quickly.

"No. Like dragons—"

Dane repeated that to his companions. Meshler was in the van. Again his head went up as Dane could see in the thin light of the half-moon; again he seemed to be sniffing. "That stink!" The word burst out of him.

Dane turned his head, coughed, and choked. Stink-stench was right! Far worse than the bad odor of the things hatched from the embryo containers, or even the smell of the ant-line—and so thick that they might be standing on the verge of an offal dump.

"There's a force field there." Tau held out the detect, and they saw that the needle quivered back and forth. So warned, Dane was able to make out the faint blue haze that formed a wall directly ahead. What faced them now was a dark, tangled mass of vegetation, but between them and it was the force field, and for that Dane was secretly glad. To plunge into that mass in the dark was more than he cared to do, whether Meshler could pilot them or not. And the stench plainly came from that direction.

"Crawler tracks turn left." Meshler followed them. Dane reluctantly did the same, Tau falling into step beside him. The Terran guessed that the medic was no more pleased with this than he was.

By now there was a road of sorts, or at least a way beaten flat by the treads of crawlers. Either one had made this trip many times, or else more than one had gone so. They paralleled the haze, which gave a wan and very ghostly light to the road they followed and the growth behind it. Light enough to—

Dane did not utter that gasp. Meshler, for all his familiarity with the wild, had voiced it, stopping short, as if the force field had swung out a sudden arm to restrain him. But Dane was as frozen.

There had been movement behind the haze. Now they looked up at something that, in that very limited light, was enough to send any sane man flying. Only for a second did they see it, and then it was gone. Dane could not be sure now he had really seen it at all. There was no sound, no movement, now. Only it was something so alien that even a star voyager flinched from facing it.

"Was it—?" Was it really there, Dane wanted to ask.

But Meshler was moving on, taking long strides so that the Terrans had to hurry to catch up, slipping and stumbling in the rutted road. It was as if the ranger was denying what he had seen, or might have seen, by that dogged advance. Nor did any of them speak. Even the brach hung quiet, a growing weight.

The haze of the force wall curved to the right, but the road kept on. Then Meshler halted again and flung out his arm as a barrier against which Dane ran. They were standing on the top of a small rise. Below them the slope grew steeper, descending to where there came the sound of water running in the night. But across the stream was a bridge, and there were very discreetly shielded lights placed at either end to mark it, diffuse-set on lowest beam. As far as the three on the height could see, there was no sentry there, which did not in the least mean that there was none in existence. Dane spoke to the brach.

"Men there?"

"No men," the brach replied promptly.

"We'll have to chance it," Meshler commented as Dane passed that along. "Chances are there is no other way of crossing the stream, or they wouldn't go to the trouble of bridging it. A crawler can usually pass through a fordable body of water."

Dane felt very naked and vulnerable as they hurried downslope, crossed the bridge, and dashed on into the welcome shadows ahead.

"We are very close to the radiation source," Tau said as

they trotted along the crawler road. "But it is more to the left."

As if his words had been an order, the path also swung left. They could still see the haze, though there was a distance between them and it at this point, a fact for which Dane was grateful. The road was now a narrow alley between two dark, looming walls of brush. It had been roughly cleared. There were the remains of roots and sapling trunks crushed and broken—wretched footing. They had to go slow here and depend once more on Meshler's night sight and his ability to lead them around trip-traps.

Here they could not see the haze, but that did not prevent Dane's imagination picturing the idea of *that* behind the growth. His half glimpse of it, he thought, was really worse to remember than perhaps a full confrontation might have been.

The track curved again, and they saw ahead diffuse lights as if on guides. Once more the brach, appealed to, stated there was no guard. But Dane hesitated and found Tau joined him in that. To the Terran, to go blundering on with no better idea of what they might face was rank folly. He said as much firmly.

"Machines," piped the brach, "machines, yes—men no."

"There you are," Meshler retorted when Dane reluctantly relayed the alien's comment. "We get in, take a crawler, and get out—if he continues to warn us."

Tau was moving the detect slowly from side to side. "If they have a snooper rigged," he said, "the other radiation covers it."

"We can't be sure they haven't," Dane persisted. The feeling that they were on the verge of a nasty trap had grown so strong in him that he could not yield to Meshler. "I'll scout ahead," the ranger returned. "Stay where you are."

They could see him as a shadow between them and the lamp glow. Then he fell to his knees and seemed to be running his hands over the rutted ground. So feeling his way ahead, he crawled to the open space by the lamps. He did not rise to his feet there but crawled back the same way.

"No ray alarm."

"How can you be so sure?"

"Fresh damar tracks. It went through that gate. If there

is any alarm, it is set for something going on two feet, or at least larger than a damar."

Dane had no idea what a damar might be, probably an animal. But Meshler was sure of his facts. And he himself with the brach reporting nothing ahead to be feared, could not hold back on a hunch alone.

So he found himself crawling on his hands and knees between the lamps, though he expected at any moment to hear some alarm, feel again the constriction of a tangle loop shooting out of the dark to bring him down. In fact, he was so sure that would happen that he could not believe they had made it, but crawled on until he nearly ran into Meshler, standing again.

"You're safe." Was there a shadow of contempt in the ranger's voice? If there was, it did not lash Dane's pride. Safety first on strange worlds was so much ingrained in any free trader that an accusation of cowardice would not set his hand seeking a stunner for reply.

With the brach still in his hold, he found it rather hard to struggle up—and was still on his knees when what he had so contantly feared happened. It was no alarm to shatter the night quiet, no physical assault from ambush.

There was a sudden flash on his left. And then, as Dane slewed around, ready to run back the way they had come, he saw the haze rise between him and the lamps, between them and the freedom that lay ahead.

They stood in a narrow corridor, walled by a force field on either side, a blind corridor, and that was beginning to close in, forcing them down the only open way—to the right, buckling in upon itself and closing, to become no corridor at all now but a wall, yet sweeping them before it as if they were in a net and that net was being drawn in by him who had cast it.

11.   SECURITY OR—?

They were being herded east, back toward the area where they had seen the monstrous thing. And to be caught in there—! Yet there was no possible way to defeat a force field.

Defeat a force field! The brachs had gotten through the weak field intended to restrain the dragons. But that was a *weak* field. This, judging by that haze, was a major lay-on of power. The only way would be to turn it off at its source. And since the source must be on the other side of the wall, they might as well give that idea up. Yet Dane kept remembering the brachs had broken that other field, seemingly only by wishing.

The three gave ground very relucantly before the relentless, if slow, push of the haze. Now they halted, and they stood under one of the trees.

"No alarms, eh?" Dane could not resist saying that. "They didn't have to have alarms. We just triggered a trap. That may be set on automatics so they don't have to worry about unexpected and uninvited visitors. Just let them be bagged and collect them later."

"If they collect them at all," Tau added. And the suggestion behind that was chilling, especially as they suspected they now shared the roaming area of that *thing*.

The brach squirmed in Dane's hold as if he found the Terran's arm about him imprisoning. His head wriggled free and pointed in the direction of the haze glowing faintly in the dark. It would not do any harm, Dane decided, to find out if the brach possibly could get through that. He relayed to the other that thought.

"The dragon screen was weak," Tau answered. "But this is full strength."

"They got in and let the dragons out—" Meshler seized

upon the optimistic side. "You think he might be able to do that for us? Come on then—!"

He caught at Dane's shoulder and gave him a push toward the force shield.

Dane spoke into the translator. "This thing, it is strong, but it is like that which was about the cage. Can you make a hole in it to let us through?"

The brach broke from Dane's hold and went to the haze, walking hesitatingly, his nose up and outstretched, as if he meant to tear through with his horn. But he halted with a good space between that horn and the mist of the barrier. Then began a slow swing of his head back and forth. He might have been measuring off the space through which to cut a door. But, as he squatted down on his haunches, the verdict piped out of Dane's mike.

"This is strong, very strong. Can maybe make small place for self—take much effort to do that. But you are too big, and cannot hold any space for long."

Dane repeated that to the others.

"So," Meshler said "it—he—can get out, but not us."

"There is another way," Dane suggested. "If he can get out, shut off the field broadcast—"

"A very long chance." Meshler sounded as if he did not believe in the success of that.

"Not too—" Tau dropped to one knee, the faint radiance of the haze making of him a silhouette. "This is a general broadcast field. The energy may be stepped up, but it is not complicated. If the brach can get through— Dane"— he turned to the younger Terran—"is there any way to make him understand what to hunt for and what he must do if he finds it?"

"If I had a light, something to draw on—"

Tau looked to Meshler. "Anything in that bag of yours to help?"

"There's a belt beamer. For the rest—" The ranger shook his head.

Dane knelt beside Tau, running his hands across the ground until one of his fingers stubbed painfully on a small stick. He pulled it out of the soil, and it came easily, so he was aware that the ground here was not iron-hard with frost.

"There is a thing"—he spoke now to the brach—"which can be done for us all."

The alien swung around, crouching between Dane and Tau. Using his glove, Dane smoothed a bit of ground. Meshler had been rummaging in the pack. Now he produced a small belt beamer. Laying it by Dane's hand, he unsealed and stripped off his outer tunic, holding this as a shield behind which they could use the light. Dane sat trying to remember force field controls. As Tau had pointed out, those were alike and the off and on switches relatively simple.

"Somewhere—not too far—" Dane began, speaking slowly and with all the distinctness he could muster, "there is a box. It will look thus." With care he used the stick to outline a force field control. "On its top are three projections, so." He added those to the sketch. "One will be turned up—thus—" He drew a short line from one dot. "The other two down, in this manner. The one that is up"—he paused to blot out the first lines and redraw them—"must be made to come down, the other two to go up. This will open the wall for us. I do not know where this box is. Perhaps you can find it, and it may be guarded by men. But it is our only hope of freedom. Do you understand?"

"Understand. But do you?" The brach's meaning was obscure. Perhaps he guessed that, for now he continued with the same desire to impress as Dane had used.

"I do this—you free. What you do then for me—for mine?"

A bargain! Dane was startled. He had forgotten that the brachs were cargo, that they really had no reason to join the crew. Come to think of it, they had not even asked the brach if he wanted to help them. They had used his particular talents as they would those of an animal as he had once been considered.

Dane explained to Tau and Meshler. The medic spoke. "But, of course. Why should we think he would automatically go on running into danger for us?"

"He freed us in that camp," cut in Meshler. "If he didn't want to help us, then why that?"

"We were something he needed." Dane thought he had the answer. "He wanted our protection in the wilderness."

"Then he'll need it now." Meshler seized upon that triumphantly. "We're all in this together."

"The conditions," Tau pointed out, "are not quite the same. That was wilderness. There must be some kind of a camp or settlement near here. He doesn't need us as much as we need him now."

"What do you want?" Paying no attention to his companions, Dane came to the point with the brach.

"No cage—be free with own—" the alien replied promptly.

The brachs were still cargo. Dane had no right to make such a decision. But neither were intelligent beings classed as cargo—they were passengers, whether the authorities agreed or not. And passengers, providing they had committed no crime on board the *Queen*, were free to go. Only he had no authority and could not make a bargain—nor give empty promises. There was expediency in trade to be sure, but there were limits past which one did not go, and the most fragile of these dealt with contacts with X-Tee races. He would stake his whole future career on any decision he made now. Perhaps Meshler did not realize that, but Dane thought Tau would when he passed along the brach's request.

"If he's intelligent," Meshler snapped, "then he had no business in a cage. Tell him 'yes' and let him get us out of *this* cage!"

But was it that simple? Suppose Dane said "yes" and the legalities of trade later said "no"? The brachs were cargo, undischarged cargo. They had a consigner on Xecho, a consignee waiting at the port. And would those tamely accept such a bargain?

"What are you waiting for?" Meshler demanded even more sharply. "If this alien can find the controls and shut off the field, he'd better get at it. Do you realize what may be in here with us?"

But Dane was not going to be pushed into what might seem betrayal in the future. He was stubborn on that point.

"I would say go free"—he tried to choose his words with care, to make certain the brach understood—"but there are those greater than I who can say I am wrong. I cannot promise they will not do that."

Tau had switched off the beamer once the drawing had been studied, and Meshler was pulling on his jacket. Dane could not see the brach, only that its nose pointed in his direction. Then came the alien's answer.

"You feel for us. Will you speak for us?"

"I will. So will all of the ship."

"More is needed."

"I cannot promise freedom that another may say no to. That would be a wrong thing. But I shall speak for you."

"Then there shall be done what can be. If this box can be found—"

The brach went to the haze, nosing around for several paces, almost as if he were sniffing for some weak spot. Then he halted, his head down, and he stood very still. Tau gave a small exclamation and caught at Dane's arm to draw his attention. On the dimly lighted dial of the detect, the needle was moving, picking up speed until it was a blur. Meshler's half-choked cry brought their eyes back to the barrier.

To Dane's sight there was no thinning of the haze, yet the brach was already halfway through and a second or two later stood on the other side. He turned to look back as if to reassure them and then trotted away in the direction they had been going when the field trapped them.

"We stay by the perimeter," Meshler advised, "but get this as a screen around us." He nodded to the brush.

What more he might have added was never to be heard, for there was a shrill tearing of the night by noise, such a shriek of insanity as Dane had never heard, sending his hands to his ears, his shoulders hunching as if that sound were a lash laid across his body.

A second shriek and Dane saw against the faint light of the haze that he was not the only one cowering from that outbreak of audio violence.

"What—what was that?" Surely as a ranger, Meshler must know the source.

"Nothing that I know." The ranger's voice was that of a badly shaken man.

"The force field is not only a trap"—Tau gave them grim understanding of what might face them now—"but it is also probably a cage. And I don't think I care to meet what we share it with."

It would be far better, Dane decided in that instant, that the owners of this trap come and take them out as prisoners.

112

They dared not get too far away from the barrier. If the brach was successful, they must be ready to make swift use of freedom. But what they were entrapped with—whatever prowled here—must also be faced. And they had no weapons.

"Fire—a torch—" That was Tau. Dane heard a crackling and saw a piece of well-leafed bush sway violently and then separate from the trunk as the medic broke it loose.

"Do you have a striker?" Tau asked Meshler.

"Green stuff—may not burn," the ranger returned. But once more he delved into the pack. "Hold it away from you —well away—"

What he did Dane could not see, but at last Meshler seemed satisfied.

"That's wet down with proto fuel. One spark and it will give you fire all right. You are right in believing that fire will hold off most beasts. Only we aren't sure what roams here. Light—the beamer—might have some effect also."

"The brach went that way," Dane said. "If we follow it along within the haze—"

"As good a way as any," Meshler agreed.

However, they did keep behind the screen of brush, and they went slowly and carefully. There had been no second outburst of the hideous screaming, yet Dane expected at any moment to confront some horror out of the night.

In a very short time the road made by the crawler treads swung away from the haze again. And they lingered at that point, not wanting to venture far from the one tie with freedom. Tau broke the silence first.

"Any camp must be over there—"

Dane saw the dark blot of Tau's arm against the haze. The medic was pointing along the curve of the road.

"Source of radiation that way."

"What I don't understand," Dane said slowly, "is how an establishment of this sort can exist and the government know nothing about it."

He expected some comment, probably an impatient one, from Meshler. When the ranger said nothing, suspicion was born.

"You do know something!" Tau put Dane's thought into words. "Is this a government project then? And if so—"

"Yes, if so, you ought to be able to get us out!"

Meshler shifted weight from one foot to the other. They could not see his expression, but there was something about his silence that fed Dane's uneasiness.

"We're waiting," Tau said.

Tau, Tau ought to be able to get to the truth! The medic's interests lay in the field of native "magic," which was, many times, thought control. He had consorted with the esper-endowed (and charlatans who were able to deceive even the astute) on many worlds. On Khatka he had unleashed his own illusions to defeat a man who believed implicitly in his own witching powers. Dane had no explanation for what he had seen Tau do to save him and Captain Jellico—and per-haps the whole world—for Limbuloo had been trying to snatch rule there.

Here the medic had no artificial aids for getting the truth out of Meshler. What he must or could do would be out of his own stock of learning. Tau could make Meshler talk if anyone on the *Queen* could.

"This territory's off limits." It seemed that Meshler would not need drastic persuasion.

"But you brought us here," Tau pointed out. "By orders?"

"No!" Meshler's denial was quick and emphatic. "It's the truth that I told you. We could not have gotten out on foot. This is the only way to survive, to try and find the experi-mental station."

"The Trosti station?"

But that, according to Meshler's own former statement, was northwest from here. Dane left the questioning wholly to Tau.

"Their secondary station, not the main one. It is a top prior-ity secret. We only know it exists, not where it is—"

"Nor what they are doing there," Tau commented. "Could it be you used our dragon hunt for a chance to do some snooping? If so, by whose orders?"

"The Council is supposed to know, but my own depart-ment—we felt—"

"That you ought to be in on any secrets, too? I wonder," Tau said speculatively, "if this is more than just interdepart-mental jealousy. No wonder there was trouble after we landed. Someone—someone important—expected us to be carrying what we dumped in the LB. Was that it?"

"I don't know." Meshler's voice was harsh. He might have

been thinking furiously and didn't want to share his thoughts, or he might be truly baffled.

"What about that hunting party? And our flitter was beamed-locked—or was it?"

"Yes! And I don't know any more about those hunters than you do." There was heat and energy in this burst. "I only know this is a top-security region."

"Yet you allowed us to send off the brach to cut out the force control, if he could," Tau persisted. "Which means one of two things: either you knew he would fail and you were buying time, or you have good suspicions about this—"

But the medic was never to complete that sentence. There was a crashing in the bush behind them and with it the same stench as that which had gagged them before. It was very apparent that the thing they had seen only momentarily was on the prowl and headed in their direction, though whether it could be definitely hunting them—

"Back!" Meshler's hand caught Dane's arm and pulled him along. "Come on!"

Once more they must depend upon the ranger's night sight, though to the left the haze gave off its glow. They made the best pace they could, only it was away from the road.

Dane held up his other arm to keep the whip of tough branches out of his face and eyes. They had already ripped at his thermo jacket and drawn blood from a thorn tear on one cheek. Then they came out of that thick growth into an open space where the moon gave them light, and the ground beneath them was smooth enough to run on.

"To the right!" That was Meshler's order. Dane obeyed, but only because he had seen it, too, something black and tall standing well above the ground. Plainly it was not growth but a sturdily based platform. Behind them, so close it assaulted their ears to deafen them, came that horrible screeching.

Meshler reached the nearest support leg of the erection, leaped up, and got a good grip on some projection Dane could not see. He climbed with speed and then something thumped down with force, which might have pinned Dane to the ground had it been inches closer. Tau caught at it.

"Ladder!" He gasped out the single word, already making use of its aid. Dane was right on his heels. Then the medic was up and over the edge of the platform, Dane not long in wriggling after. A push sent him rolling to one side as the ranger grabbed the ladder, jerking it aloft.

Dane, still lying flat, wormed his way to the edge to watch for what might exit into the thin moonlight on their trail. It came, a hunched shape moving as a black blot. It was hard to gauge its bulk from their perch, but that it was several times his own size Dane would swear. Though it had exited from cover on four feet, it rose a little to shuffle on two, the forelimbs dangling loosely as it came.

The thing did not raise its head far enough for Dane to make out anything but a dark blob, and he was just as well pleased that this was so, for the very outlines suggested that it was a nightmare creature, while the stench of it made him sick.

Now and then it went to fours again, and he thought it did not hunt by sight but rather by scent, and it was nosing them out. Finally it came to the standards below the platform. If it could climb, how could they fight it off? Even though he had not been able to assess its natural weapons, there was that about it that suggested even to an armed man that it would prove a formidable opponent. Meshler had been able to climb without the ladder. Could it?

An appalling shriek broke from immediately under them, and the platform itself quivered—not from the sound, but because some heavy force beat at one of its supports. Dane dared not lean over far enough to see what was going on below, but it felt as if the creature was working to either pull down or push over the nearest pillar-leg of the four supporting their perch. The blows or jerks were enough to set it shuddering and swinging.

Thud-jerk-thud! The creature persisted. How long before that would pay off and the platform would collapse, taking them with it? They were cornered up here. Yet the move to climb had seemed the best escape.

"Look!" Tau's hand on him pulled Dane around a little. The medic was lying flat, too, as if he thought they had a better chance of not being shaken loose that way.

Look? Where? At what? Patrol men descending via grav belts to their rescue? This venture had already taken on so many of the incredible elements of a tridee show that Dane could expect that traditional ending to extreme danger to be a part of it.

But what he did see was a green-white glowing spot at or near where the monster had earlier emerged.

12. HIDDEN BASE

The platform shuddered under them, and Dane wondered how long it would be before it gave way under the determined assault of the thing below. Meanwhile, that phosphorescent greenish blob flowed farther into the open.

Flowed was the best description of its progress. It was unstable in outline, as if it were a mass of some semiliquid substance, and the closer it approached, the less it resembled any living creature Dane knew.

Now another odor warred with the stench of the first comer—as foul. There was a sudden halt in the thumping of the support. Once more came the screech. From their perch they could not see the monster below, but Dane guessed that what approached was no companion it welcomed.

The flowing mass was huge, and its glow gave it visibility in the night. It was, Dane speculated, about the size of the wrecked flitter. As it neared the platform, it now and then put out projections of quivering material, white and brighter than the main bulk of its body. All of these inclined one way, pointing at the monster under them. But none held position long, instead sinking back into the general mass, as if such effort was more than it could summon for any length of time.

Again the monster screeched, but it did not charge to do battle with the newcomer, nor did it flee. It was as if it hesitated, not quite sure of the safest course.

The blob made excellent time across the open. More and more of the projections appeared, to point tips forward. The projections grew thinner, developing distinct tips, taking on the style of tentacles, though still they did not stay aloft for long.

A third screech and the monster seemed to have made up its mind. It shot forward to the right with a speed that made it just a dark blur, a dark arm and limb streaking down across the blob as it passed, cutting cleanly, and throwing off the stuff of at least three tentacles, which hit the ground and began a movement of its own, forming a small mass like the parent body. But the monster paid no attention to that. It faced about, its forelimbs up and whirling out, as the blob altered course, heading with less speed but with inexorable purpose for it.

Once more the first comer made a lightning-swift attack, shearing and tossing aside what it cut away from the blob. Again those fragments combined to become a smaller blob, moving as the first cutting had done toward the monster.

The monster was facing now not one opponent but three, though the two small ones would seem to be far less dangerous than the main body. Twice more the thing struck, ripping at its opponent in a frenzy, and each time it only created a new, if much smaller, enemy.

"They have it ringed!" Meshler cried out. "It may think it's cutting that other thing to pieces, but it's really ringing itself in."

He was right. The first three blobs had become eighteen. The monster no longer attacked with the same speed. Either it was tiring, its energy perhaps already somewhat worn by its battle with the platform support, or else it was growing more wary, perhaps beginning to understand, if it had a mind to comprehend, that its efforts put it in more and more danger.

The blob now, the parent one, was less than half the size it had been when it oozed into the open. But as it shrank, its offspring increased. Now the larger of those were beginning to sprout short, wavering tentacles in turn. And always those pointed to the creature around which they had built a ring.

There came a pause in that weird struggle. The monster squatted motionless now, still facing the first blob. The others did not move. Instead the first tentacles they put forth, to point small fingers at their enemy, now waved to each side, spinning thinner and thinner, weaving back and forth aimlessly through the air. But that there was method in this was quickly demonstrated. Two weaving tentacles from separate smaller blobs touched. Instantly they united, so that the two became one, thin and closer to the ground. And as they had managed this unification, so did the rest. Thus the ring about their enemy was complete, save for directly before the monster, where the parent blob lay. Perhaps its inertia was meant to lull the victim. It would seem that way, for the first comer apparently did not see or care that three-quarters of the way around, it was now encircled by a ribbon band lying on the ground, momentarily quiescent.

What signal passed to produce the next move in that struggle Dane did not know, but the two loose ends of that band flew to join themselves to the parent. As an over-stretched piece of elastic material might do, the band itself snapped against the back of the squatting monster, pushing it forward, screeching and flailing wildly, until the front portion of the blob raised up, not tentacles but half its bulk, to come down with smashing finality on its captive. It heaved and rolled from side to side, the band now completely reunited.

Though engulfed, the monster had not surrendered. The rolling blob spun around, changing shape constantly as the struggle within it beat and tore at its heart. But that struggle gradually subsided. The blob tightened, drew in and in until it was a solid-looking sphere, and there was no more movement.

"Digesting," Tau said. "Well, we've seen how you *don't* fight that anyway."

"What is it?" Dane turned to Meshler for enlightenment. He should know something of the native wildlife.

"I don't know." The ranger was still staring, bemused, at the ball. "It is not native here."

"That makes two—three, if you count what it ate," Dane said. "That antline and these two. The antline was certainly from off-world, maybe these, too."

"But"—Meshler turned his head as if it was a distinct effort to do so—"it is against the law to import without a certificate. The Trosti people would not—"

"Who said these were imported, or—if so—in these forms?" Tau asked. "If they have a box, these could be retrogressions of things entirely different. The Trosti people have a high reputation, of course, but are you entirely sure, Meshler, that this is a Trosti undertaking?"

"This is top-security country under Trosti management," the ranger said slowly.

"Orders can be used as a screen at times," commented the medic, and in that he was reflecting what the free traders had learned long ago.

"Why would anyone want monsters?" Dane looked to the blob and then away. He didn't like to remember the details of that recent struggle, though he had no sympathy for the monster who had lost.

"Maybe not monsters for the sake of monsters," Tau acknowledged. "These are probably experiments of some sort. But there are other uses for such radiation. Suppose such a box were planted on a holding, how long could a settler stick it out if his livestock began to mutate to this extent? It would be an excellent way to clear off a world. Or, if they could make it work on human beings—"

Dane sat up. Tau was giving voice to fears he shared. But Meshler was more interested in the first part of the medic's speculation.

"Why would they want to get rid of settlers?"

"You know more about your own planet than I do. Ask yourself that. I am wondering whether that thing can climb," Tau watched the blob. "Also how long before it is hungry again—"

Dane stood up. There were huge reptiles on his native world, which, engorging a large meal, were then sluggish for days thereafter. One could never judge unknown fauna by what one knew of other species, but they could hope this was the case now. He turned to look for the haze marking the barrier. They should be able to see it from here and mark out a path if the brach was successful and the force field went out.

"There is no reason—" Meshler was still wrestling with the problem of the settlers being the target. "There is no reason here. And this, this kind of experiment, it can't be known by the Council."

"Good. Let us get out, and you can tell them all about it," replied Tau. "Is the field still up," he asked Dane.

"Yes." The thin haze was unbroken. How long before they must conclude that the brach had failed? And how long before that blob would uncoil and be hungry again? Could it climb? He would rather not guess, though his treacherous imagination kept suggesting that there was no reason in the world to believe it could not.

Resolutely he concentrated on the matter at hand, to calculate the nearest point of the haze. He thought that lay to the north, and he said as much.

"The question is, do we stay here, or do we try to reach the field before our visitor comes out of his after dinner trance," Tau said. "I'm wondering how many more surprises may be lurking in the undergrowth."

He had gotten so far when Dane saw the flicker of the haze. Had the brach been successful? But the barrier steadied, and he choked back his cry, only to see a second flicker before the force field disappeared.

"It's off!"

"We move!" Tau stooped to pick up something Meshler had laid beside his pack. It was the torch made from the branch. The medic weighed it in one hand, as if he meditated its use as a club, then thrust the butt in his belt.

Dane took a careful bearing on the nearest point of freedom. Beyond that the land was clear, and they could make better time. He gave a last glance at the blob, but that remained so quiet that one could believe it a rock outcrop.

He kicked the ladder out, feeling its weighted end thump on the ground, and swung over. But as he descended, he continued to peer between the supports to watch the blob. He wished that they did not have to turn their backs on the thing to flee.

There was thick brush between them and the open, matted stuff through which Meshler had earlier guided them. As they ran for that, Tau pulled the torch from his belt.

"How inflammable is this woods?" He came level with the ranger to ask.

"This is winter, and the leaves are dried. They will fall in the spring when pushed off by new growth. What would you do?"

"Set a wall behind us—make sure we won't be ambushed by other nasty surprises."

Again they locked hands, and Meshler led them through the bush. When they could see the open land, Tau brought from one of the loops of his belt a sparker and touched it to the soaked torch. The thing blazed fiercely, and the medic turned, whirled it about his head, and hurled it into the thicket through which they had forced their way.

"That's a perfect beacon," Dane protested.

"Maybe so, but it's the best answer, short of setting on the field again—which we can't do—to deter a tracker. I don't fancy anything from that horror pen sniffing on my trail!"

They ran, speeding out into the open. When they stumbled into the road left by the crawlers, there was a growing line of fire behind.

"Where now?" Dane fully expected Meshler to turn back to the lamp-guarded way. But instead he faced in the other direction.

"We still need transportation—more than ever if they hunt us down after that—" He gestured to the fire, not only spreading a red and yellow ring at ground level, but also now setting tall candles by igniting trees.

"We just walk in and ask—" Dane stood where he was. "That's about as stupid as kicking that blob—"

"No." At least Meshler had some sense left. "We wait." He looked about, hitching the pack off his shoulder. "That place up there might do."

The place up there was a cut made by crawler treads running between slightly higher banks. There was cover, though of a meager sort, in some crumbling ridges of soil. Had they blasters, it would have been a place for an ambush. Was Meshler thinking that the fire would draw attention—bring a vehicle here they could take? But without weapons—?

"What will you do?" he demanded. "Wave them down?"

For the first time he heard a rusty noise. Could it be that Meshler was laughing?

"Something like that. If we are lucky and someone comes to see what is happening."

He took something from his pack, but what it was Dane could not see. It appeared the ranger was not going to explain his plan. The sensible thing was to jet off—he and Tau—and leave Meshler to his folly, but they were not left time for decision. The clank of a crawler in operation came to their ears.

With Tau, Dane speedily took cover behind the all-too-slight ridge. The ranger was on the other side of the road and had so well melted into the landscape that Dane had no idea where he lay.

Whoever drove the crawler was pushing that machine to its top speed. The engine and frame were protesting the resulting shaking with a medley of small noises. They could see it nosing into the cut, and it clanked on past them, while Dane waited tensely for Meshler's attack. When that did not come, he gave a sigh of relief. The ranger must have thought better of his wild idea.

As the crawler continued, a dark shape separated from the opposite ridge and came down into the road. What followed Dane could not see clearly, but he thought that Meshler had tossed something on the rear of the machine. The crawler ground on for a couple of rounds of its treads, and then vapor began to wreathe in it.

From the cabin sounded coughing and shouts indistinguishable to the Terrans. The door swung open on one side, and a man threw himself out and rolled to the ground, followed by another. There was a spat of blaster fire aimed straight up into the night. By that Dane saw two more men drop from the cabin, clawing at their faces and yelling. The blaster fell from the grip of whoever had held it and lay in one of the ruts, beaming its deadly ray along the ground, sending the full of its charge back within the narrow walls of that deep track.

Reflection from that continued to give them a limited view of what was going on. The crawler, cabin doors hanging open, kept on, but the men who had fallen or jumped from it were lying still. Two more had made valiant efforts to draw hand weapons. One got his free of the holster before he went limp.

Now Meshler appeared, sprinting along beside the road, leaping for the crawler, catching an open door, being dragged until he pulled himself up to wriggle in. The heavy machine ground to a stop.

The blaster still continued to discharge fire along the rut, and the two Terrans made a careful detour by that ribbon of radiance as they ran to join the ranger. Tau paused by the first of the crumpled figures. He did not stoop to touch the man, only sniffed and then hurriedly drew a succession of quick breaths to clear his lungs.

"Sleep gas," he said to Dane. "So he did have a weapon."

"And used it brilliantly!" Dane was willing to give credit. But what if only one of those in the crawler had had time to really aim? Meshler could easily have been crisped. He went down on one knee, caught at the discharging blaster, and thumbed it off. With the failure of that light, he had to feel his way from one body to the next, collecting the rest of their weapons.

But in spite of recklessness, Meshler had made his venture pay off handsomely. They had the crawler, plus four blasters, though one was close to power exhaustion, transportation, and arms.

Only Meshler was not yet satisfied, it seemed, when the Terrans joined him. The crawler had come to life again and was slowly edging around. The ranger only grunted, as if thinking of something else when the Terrans congratulated him on his success.

"Clear them off the road, will you," he said when the machine was turned to face its source. "Stow them well up on the ridge. They'll sleep it off."

"But where are you planning to go?" Dane demanded.

"You know how fast one of these moves?" There was a shade of contempt in that question. "We can take it, sure. And then they can retake us, long before we reach Cartl's. We need a flitter, or a shuttle flier—"

"You believe we can just ride into their camp and pick out the kind of transportation we want?" snapped Dane.

"Won't know until we try, will we?" Meshler sounded reasonable, but reason and what he suggested had no common base. "Crawler came out with their men in it—crawler comes back. Who's to know it isn't their men coming back? And you have blasters—"

Oh, it was all logical in an insane kind of way. The Terrans could pull the blasters on Meshler, but the ranger probably knew they would not. And the crawler *was* slow transport.

"Light two prayer sticks to Xampbrema," Tau commented. "Beat the drum, summon the seven spirits of Alba Nuc—" He might have been reciting one of the spells he had culled over the years. "He's mad enough to try it. We might as well aid and abet him."

Together Dane and Tau carried the sleepers to one of the ridges, stretching them out to await dawn or whatever waking hour the gas allowed them, while, under Meshler's guidance, the crawler waddled past the scene of the ambush.

Anyway, he did, as Meshler had pointed out, now have a blaster, thought Dane, as he climbed into the cabin. And the—the brach! In the push of late events, he had forgotten the brach. Somewhere the alien must be—they could not pull out and leave him.

What the crawler, following its own rutted trail, brought them to was a basin, oval in shape. But when they stared down, Dane shook his head and rubbed his eyes. There was something there—

"Take it in quick!" Tau gave that order sharply, as if they were confronted by danger.

The crawler's nose dipped. There was a strange feeling of disorientation, almost akin to that one felt on entering hyper. But they were not on board ship now.

Dane had closed his eyes almost involuntarily to keep out that queer feeling. Now he opened them, realizing the crawler was descending a steep slope.

What lay before them was no longer affected, or else he was not affected, by the dizzying blurring that had struck moments earlier. There were diffuse lamps out, none of them on high, yet strong enough to have provided a beacon reaching above the level of the basin's rim. Only they had not seen them. They had been in the dark until they slipped through that thing which acted as a lid over the valley basin.

"A sight-distort," Tau murmured. "A wide-scale distort. This place could not be seen by a flier."

But Dane was more interested now in what lay ahead. The lamps marked four bubble structures, the usual shelters carried by any scouting camp. Beyond those were two buildings that looked, so low were their walls and those roofed with earth, as if they were more excavated in the ground than built above the surface.

What was more important now was a vehicle park to one side. There was another crawler there, and beyond it a flitter, and farther still— Dane gave a muffled exclamation, for the surface of the ground had been hollowed out and in that large pit, balanced on its fins, was a spacer. The diffuse lamps near the rim showed the glassy, congealed earth, proving that the ship had planeted here more than once. Many blast-offs and setdowns, with the pilot riding in on deter rockets, had built up that burn.

"The flitter—" Meshler nodded as if he had known all along their amazing luck was going to hold.

But the camp was in nowise deserted. Men were hurrying to the other crawler. Dane distinctly saw in the light the long barrel of a disrupter, though what such a weapon, forbidden for civilian use, was doing here was just more of the puzzle. Also, from one of the earth-roofed buildings rose a rod shining metallically in the light. That was a power com send, by its length able not only to reach the port in the north but also perhaps to beam messages into space.

Meshler kept the crawler at its steady pace. They would have to pass close to the other vehicle in order to reach the flitter, and he made no attempt to swing wide. Perhaps he thought their bluff would hold.

The other machine, which had started up, ground to a halt as they approached, and a man leaned out of its cabin to shout at them. Meshler waved his hand through the window. Perhaps he hoped that ambiguous gesture would buy them a little more time. The bulk of the crawler and its walls would protect them for a little. But once they left it to run to the flitter—

Dane's blaster was ready. He measured the distance yet remaining, and then Meshler brought the nose of the crawler around, aiming it so that its body would provide them with shelter. The shouting from the other machine grew louder, more insistent. Then a vicious spat of blaster fire cut the ground warningly before their nose in a signal to stop.

Tau slammed the door open. "Now!" He was out and running for the flitter.

13. WILDERNESS REFUGE

Dane pulled his hood around so that his lips were set against the interpreter's mike.

"Brach—to the flitter!" He did not know where the alien

was. Perhaps he had already fled the camp. But if not, Dane had to give him his chance. "To the flitter, brach!"

"Get going!" Meshler tried to shove Dane from the cabin. But the Terran clung stubbornly to his seat and gestured the ranger to go on.

"Brach—come to the flitter!" He signaled once more while fending off a push from Meshler.

With a hot exclamation, the ranger elbowed past Dane and ran as Tau had done, but halfway to the flitter, he turned and aimed a pencil of blaster fire at the foreground, lashing a smoking trench across the soil to slow those coming to take them.

"Brach!" Dane could wait no longer. He dropped from the cabin and zigzagged a pattern toward the flitter with flares of blasters cutting right and left. They were not aiming to take prisoners—they were out to kill.

Before he reached the open door of the flitter cabin, something streaked for the craft, and Dane, with a leap of heart, knew it for the brach.

Somehow they tumbled in together, but this time Tau, having reached the flitter first, was at the controls. He must have hit the rise button full force, for they took off straight up with a lift that had some of the power of a spacer's take-off, pinning them for an instant or two to the seats over which they sprawled in a squirming mixture of men and brach.

Before they were sorted out, the flitter was screaming into the early morning at the highest speed it could maintain in a wild race to put distance between them and the camp.

"We're away, I think!" Tau said as they spiraled into a graying sky. "I didn't see another flitter, and unless they can draw us with another ground beam—"

"Which they must have. Remember how they got us before," countered Dane. He expected every second to feel that compelling drag on them once again, bringing them earthward. Why did Meshler believe they could escape when that had happened before? Now that he had time to think, Dane was puzzled. Surely the ranger had not forgotten—

"North and east—" Meshler, as if believing they had nothing to fear now, leaned over to inspect the direction dial. Tau obediently adjusted their course until the needle hit the proper marking.

The brach had subsided against Dane. He could feel him gasping with the effort of that last dash. The alien was a weight on his lap, and he drew the edges of his jacket about him.

"No ground beam—" Dane could not understand how they had made so clean an escape.

"Not yet anyway," commented Tau. In the subdued light the expression on the medic's face suggested that he, too, expected momentarily seizure by that force. Nor did they relax even as the minutes sped by and the pull did not clamp them.

"Get to Cartl's," Meshler said, but more as if he were talking to himself than to them. "Beam in to port with their com—"

"Report what?" Dane demanded. "Your authorities must have some knowledge of all this—"

"But do they?" Tau cut in thoughtfully. "It wouldn't be the first time that research techs went beyond the agreed-upon boundaries, and it wouldn't be the first time they got in deeper than they planned."

"Or sold out—" Meshler added bleakly.

"Sold out to whom?" Dane wanted to know. "And why?"

But the ranger merely shook his head. That he had been shaken by the events of the past night was plain. His pragmatic approach at the LB was long since lost. What he had seen here must have proven that the story told by the *Queen*'s crew was true and that there was far more going on in the wilderness of his own planet than his service, pledged to the regulation and patrol of that same country, knew.

"That force barrier," he said now. "Can you tell with that detect whether it is up again or not."

"No. It will pick up radiation but not specify as to any one kind. I cannot be sure without altering it which radiation is the field."

"There might be one way." Dane turned his head to speak into the translator. The brach still wore his twin mike against his throat.

"The box—you left the levers so—"

"No, not could do—"

"How so?"

"Men come and go. Could find easy. Turn back—so." The brach dipped his head, pantomiming use of the horn. "No box working now."

Dane heard a harsh whistle of breath from Meshler when he passed this information along.

"Cartl's." The ranger leaned forward as if by the very force of his will he could hurl them even faster toward their goal. "Have to get to Cartl's with a warning!"

Then the reason for his anxiety hit the two Terrans.

"Those monsters!" Dane exclaimed.

"How many of them—" Tau added.

Freed from the force wall, could they be rounded up again by the men in the basin? Could such as the blob be handled—unless they just blastered it? And as Tau had said, how many—or what kinds—had been in there? Raised and tended perhaps? There was that antline—had it been an earlier escapee wandering north?

"How many and what kind are right," Meshler said grimly. "We shall have to warn all the southmost holdings. And we have no idea of what they may have to face."

"Unless you can get who's responsible for it and pry some facts out of him," Tau returned. "This holding does have a direct com to the port?"

"They all have," Meshler answered.

Day was dawning, but it was not to be a clear one. Clouds drew in between them and the weak winter sun, and then suddenly they were curtained by sleet, icing quickly one outer shell of the flitter. There was no visibility, and Tau pointed to the altimeter.

"We are being forced down."

"But we are still on course," Meshler returned. "Keep going."

Not only did the waves of sleet break about their craft, but there was also a wind coming in gusts, which pushed them off course, so that Tau had to fight the controls to bring them back time and time again. It was as if the weather was a weapon used with purpose to keep them from their goal.

But such weather might also deter the monsters from wandering too far from the cover the woods behind the vanished force field offered.

Tau was watching the radar as well as the altimeter, his

head turning quickly. "We may have to set down," he warned. "That or chance crashing."

Dane had never been airborne in such a storm, and as the fury increased, he could well believe they might be smashed to the ground by one of those punishing gusts. He wondered if they *could* set down safely. There was no way of telling whether they were over wooded or open land.

"Here goes!" Tau waited for no agreement from his companions. He battled the gusts, fighting the worst fury of wind and sleet, watching the radar that was their only guide to what might lie below. At least they were not in mountain country, though Dane judged they were far off the course Meshler had ordered. Instead of heading northwest, they were being pushed south.

At top speed for the flitter and at what altitude Tau could win for them, they fled along the easiest path the storm would allow—south. And how long that period of struggle in the darkness of storm, none of them knew.

But the sleet finally vanished, leaving traces of its passing in the icy casing on the cabin windows, so they were flying blind, with only instruments to guide them.

"Set down while we can," Tau urged. "If that hits again, we may not be able to take it. We're too iced up to handle well aloft."

"All right. If you can make it," Meshler replied grudgingly.

Dane's shoulder ached with tension. He wanted the controls under his own hands. Tau could pilot—every man aboard the *Queen* could—but now to sit there without any chance of changing destiny and wait for the end— He had to nerve himself to be quiet.

The medic would have to hold them on hover and watch the radar for a clear setdown. But to hold on hover in any kind of heavy wind was near to impossible. The grim line of Tau's mouth suggested that he knew the worst of what might happen.

They went on hover, and straightway the craft nearly overturned under a mighty gust. But luckily that was not followed by a second. Meshler leaned far forward, his nose almost touching the radar dial as if such proximity might actually force the reading to one they must have.

"Now!" He barked out the order.

They were setting down, Dane knew that. With great

willpower he did not look at the dials or watch Tau fighting the controls. He had hooked the safety belt around him and the brach, saw Meshler, for the second time since this venture had begun, hit a button controlling safe-foam, and waited while that padding fluffed up about them.

But the stuff did not have time to reach shoulder level before, with a jolt that whipped them back in their seats, they touched solid surface. With that thud a large section of the encasing ice on the cabin windows cracked and fell away.

What faced them was a thick wall of vegetation, so near that the branch tips appeared to be scratching at the cabin. Dane opened the door to allow the safe-foam to spill out, and a lash of iced rain cut in at them. He loosened the brach and pushed the alien into the second seat of the flitter. Then, pulling up his hood and lowering the visor, he climbed out to see just where Tau had brought them down.

A moment later he stood frozen by more than the wind and rain, by the sense of just how much luck had favored them, for when he turned his attention to the tail of the flitter, he saw the lip of a drop. They had reached ground on a wedge of rock that was thrust out into a veiling mist and had come down facing a tangle of growth. So small was that island of safety that Dane blinked and blinked again, almost unable to believe they had made it at all.

The rock under foot was treacherous with a skim of freezing rain, but his space boots kept him upright as, with his gloved hands on the flitter, he worked his way back to the tail and that drop, not daring to approach the rim any closer than he needed to get around the flitter and slip to the other side. That exploration told him no more than he had discovered at first. They had made a precarious landing on a wedge of rock protruding into space, with thick vegetation before them. And already ice was forming to lock the tripod of landing gear to the rock.

Meshler and Tau had begun the same crawl around the craft, sloshing first through the foam, which piled in thick suds below the door. That was beaten down by the rain but did not wholly disappear, curdling rather into frozen strips. When the other two reached Dane, Tau's face was a little green under the visor, and Meshler was slowly shaking his head.

"By all the Laws of Legester!" the ranger exclaimed. "Such fortune I have never seen before. The length of my hand, my foot, one way or the other—" He shook his head, staring at the flitter against which he steadied himself with both hands, as if he expected it to perhaps turn into a raging antline or something of the sort.

"They say"—Tau's voice sounded remote—"that if a man is born to drown, he will not die by blaster. It seems that there is reason to believe we are not yet designed to die. Now"—he turned to Meshler and became more brisk—"have you any idea of where we may be?"

"Well away from our course—south and west. That is the most I can say. And before we take off again, we shall have to have better weather. How long that will be—" He shrugged.

"*If* we take off," Dane corrected. Using great care, he had squatted down to peer under the belly of the craft at the tripod landing gear. It was certainly icing up around that, and some of the curdled foam had seeped there, adding to the bulk of slush and freezing sleet. It must be that this wedge of rock had a drain toward the center, where the flitter rested. Before they took off, that would have to be defrosted carefully. He pointed out that fact when the other two hunched down to see.

"At least it is an anchor now. The more it freezes fast, the less chance we have of being swept off yonder." Tau gestured at the edge of the wedge. "We wait out the storm, and then we can cut her loose and take off. But we'd better get inside now."

He was right. The cold pierced even thermo clothing. They shook off all the moisture they could and climbed back into the flitter, which now and again rocked ominously under the push of the wind. Would any gust be strong enough to tear them from their frozen anchorage?

Meshler shared out another tube of E ration. And Dane, exploring the storage compartment, found they were not too badly off for supplies, even if the small pack Meshler had shouldered was exhausted. There was an E-ration box and one of medical supplies, a pair of distance lenses and some extra blaster charges.

"They did well by us," he commented as he restored most of what he had found to the compartment. "What about

the com? Can't you call that holding, give them the information, and ask them to relay it?"

Meshler had taken the pilot's seat on their return to the
flitter. Now he threw back his hood and loosened his jacket.

"This storm would blanket any call. But as soon as it is
over— We can sleep it out."

It was only sensible. And, at the very mention of sleep,
Dane felt suddenly as if he must have it. It had certainly
been more than twenty-four hours since they had holed up
between the rocks for those cramped periods of rest. But as
the flitter shuddered under wind blasts now and then, he
wondered if they could sleep—knowing that they might be
hurled over the drop.

But he did sleep, and so did the others. When he stirred
into wakefulness, it was a few seconds before memory caught
up and he knew where he was. The flitter no longer trembled
under the wind, nor could he hear the drum of rain on its
surface. He elbowed his way up, the warm weight of the
brach lying across him. The alien snuffled and made a small
whimper of complaint. However, Dane was able to see
through the window—or he could have seen had not a solid
surface of sparkling frost curtained it. So bright was it that
he thought it must be sunlight, and if the storm was over, it
was time for them to be on their way. His movements
jogged the front seat, and Tau raised his head from its back,
coughed, and looked around.

"What—" he began, and then seemed to realize his surroundings.

"Sun out there—maybe—" Dane pointed to the window.

Tau slewed around and felt for the door catch. It resisted
as if the cold had formed an additional lock, then gave way.
Tau pushed the door open, and there was not only an intense cold that made them gasp, but also sun that shone
straight into their eyes.

The medic swung down a long leg and was half out of
the cabin when he slipped, grabbing desperately for the
edge of the door. Though he went with a bone-jarring thud
to his knees, he kept his hold, lying across the door opening.

With difficulty he wriggled around to look outside, and
when Dane saw his face, Tau had the expression of a man
who had felt blaster rays within searing distance. With in-

finite care he drew back, seemingly unable to move his legs, drawing himself up with his arms until he was again on the cabin seat. Then he jerked the door shut.

"Glare ice," he reported. "I don't think anyone could stand, let alone walk, on that."

Meshler forced open the door on his side and stared down at the surface below. "Same over here," he reported.

"The running gear will have to be loosened before we lift," Dane said. "Blaster fire at low level?" He made that into a question.

"Need some kind of lifeline for the one doing it," Tau commented. "What about the supplies?"

Dane pushed the brach gently to one side and opened the cubby he had explored the night before. He had not remembered seeing anything of the sort, but it might have been there. Only there was nothing.

"What's that?" Meshler had squirmed around in his seat and was pointing over Dane's head at something thickly rolled. The Terran pulled at it and discovered he had tugged loose the end of a many times folded weatherproof plasta sheet—perhaps intended to be pegged down over the flitter in times of storm. The flitter in the *Queen* had not carried such equipment.

"Cut this into strips, knot it, and we have our rope." Meshler brought a long-bladed, sharp knife from his belt, ready to work.

But it was hard labor, since the plasta, tough enough to withstand extremes of weather, did not yield easily even to so keen a blade. The ranger sawed with patience until he had three unevenly cut strips, which he knotted, the material again resisting, into a crude and bulky rope. He, without suggesting any volunteering for venturing out to burn off the landing gear, tied this in turn to his own belt, snapped down his visor, tightened his overjacket against the cold, and saw that Tau and Dane had good hold of the other end of the line.

"It should not be a long job—with this." He had a blaster ready in his gloved hand. Once more he opened the door and slipped out. Although he kept one hand on the frame to steady himself, it was apparent he could not keep his balance.

Dane and Tau braced. The rope twisted about their

wrists, their bare hands gripping the ragged edges. Meshler tried to take a step, lost his footing, and disappeared from sight, his weight pulling on them both as they tensed against that tug.

The rope jerked and twisted, as if Meshler were wriggling about, but the two in the cabin held it as taut as they could. How long would it take him to melt away the ice? Dane felt the ache in his arms. His wrists had gone white and were turning numb where the plasta cut in.

Then, when the Terran thought the pressure was crippling him, an arm showed at the door, a hand grasped a hold, and Meshler pulled himself in, to collapse on his seat, while Dane leaned over and banged the door shut. The ranger shook himself, shed his gloves, and sat up. He thumbed the takeoff, and Dane was thrown back, half on the brach, who let out a cry and tried to roll away.

They were up, rising steadily, though they could only guess that by the feel. The frosted windows still held away the morning.

"We were driven south," Meshler said. "Therefore, we go north, though I am not sure how far west we were pushed."

"How about the com?" Tau asked.

Meshler detached the board mike and snapped the pilot's throat latch at his neck.

"Calling Cartl—Cartl—Cartl." He made a kind of song of the name.

As one they waited for any reply. But what came was a harsh jangle of noise, almost as shattering to the ear, though not on the same scale, as the screech of the monster.

"Interference." Meshler dropped his finger from the call button. "Nothing can get through that."

"Normal?" Tau wanted to know.

"How can I tell?" The ranger's old impatience flared. His eyes were a little sunken, and his face was thinned down, as if he had aged months since their meeting. "This is new country to me. But that is so loud and persistent, I would say it was intended."

"They may be expecting us to broadcast a warning," the medic suggested. "Well, it's up to us to go in ourselves, as long as we can't send a message."

North because they had been driven south, east because Meshler was sure they had also flown west. But how could the ranger be sure? There was no beam to ride. If he had managed to get in touch with the holding, they could have used a broadcast as a beacon. Now they had nothing but the ranger's guessing, and the country under them was un-explored wilderness—unless it held some more surprises, such as the basin camp.

At least they had no storm, and as they went, the windows of the cabin slowly lost their frost crust, so they could see it was a particularly clear day. Meshler found a small visa screen, usable in such weather, and focused it so that they could see the country below.

Judging by the sun, they knew it was early morning, which meant that they had slept away part of the day before as well as the intervening night—a loss of time that worried Meshler, though with all the territory lying between the basin and Cartl's, he surely could not expect any of the creatures released there to have already covered that distance.

They caught no sign of the basin under the distort, nor were there any other machines in the air, no sign of crawlers or crawler tracks on the ground. There was a uniform land-scape of patchy forest cut by two rivers of good size, plus here and there open rocky stretches—and no sign that this was anything but the wilderness Meshler claimed.

14. CARTL'S HOLDING

From time to time the ranger tried the com, only to meet the crackle of interference. But suddenly he indicated an ice-edged river.

"The Veecorox!"

"You've seen that before?" inquired Tau.

Perhaps, thought Dane, the medic was now as uneasy as he over their very vague route.

"An expedition got this far last year." Meshler settled back in the pilot's seat with a relaxation that could have been relief. The ranger must have been just as disturbed as they about their unknown course.

"We have only to follow this to where the tributary, the Corox, feeds in, then turn east. That is the beginning of Cartl's land."

He banked the flitter and turned to follow the river. The land under them showed no signs that men had ever ventured this far.

"Your southland is largely wilderness then," commented the medic.

"It is hard to clear land—to import machinery is wasteful. We cannot keep bringing in fuel and techs to service the machines or repair parts. And horses or duocorns from Astra or any of the off-world draft animals do not do well here— not in the first generation, anyway. They have been trying to breed some at the Ag stations, to develop a strain that can live here without being constantly cared for. There is a native insect, the tork fly, which goes for their eyes. So far we haven't been able to build up any immunity in imports. There are no native animals that can be used for heavy labor. The result is that the holdings have machinery in community ownership and move the pieces from place to place for clearing. Then in some dry seasons they try a burn-off; only that must be controlled, which means an army of men on the job."

"So settlements have not advanced much since First Ship," commented Tau.

Dane saw the line along the ranger's jaw tighten, as if he were biting back some hot and hasty comment, and then Meshler replied.

"Trewsworld's done enough to keep autonomous. We won't go up for any resettlement auction, if that's what you mean." Then he paused, looked to Tau, and Dane saw a shade of worry on his face. "You think—that might be it?"

"A chance, is it not?" Tau asked. "Suppose what you have so hardly won could be lost, or even a part of it? Enough so you could not claim autonomy any more?"

Dane understood. Any planet under pioneer settlement had to grow, to show appreciable gains each year in size of population and then in exports, or else the Grand Department of Immigration could legally put it up for auction.

Then if the settlers could not match an outside bid, they lost all they had worked so hard to gain.

"But why?" asked Meshler. "We're an Ag planet. Anyone else here would face the very same difficulties we have been fighting from the first. There's nothing to attract outsiders—no minerals worth that much for exploiting—"

"What about the rock from the sealed compartment of the prospectors' crawler?" Dane asked. "They had found something they thought rich enough to lock in. They were killed, and that was taken. Perhaps there is more here on Trewsworld than you know, Meshler."

The ranger shook his head. "A mineral survey was run by detect on second survey. There are normal amounts of iron, copper, other ores, but nothing worth shipping off-world. We use what we can ourselves. Besides, those men may not have been blasted for what they carried but what they saw and the rock taken to confuse us. You said the antline was roaming near there. They might have run into a party trying to get it back."

"Perfectly possible," agreed Tau. "At the same time, I would suggest that another minerals' survey be run—if you are left time to do it."

"The basin camp," Dane said, "was not a recent setup. How long have the Trosti people been here?"

"Eight years—planet time."

"And how about any new holdings cut in their direction during that time?" Now Tau had given him the clue Dane was groping for.

"Cartl—let's see. Cartl had his clearing gathering in the spring of '24, before grass growth. And this is '29. He has the southmost holding."

"Five years then. How about other holdings—east, west, north?"

"North is too cold for lathsmers. They have only a couple of experimental Ag stations north of the port," Meshler answered promptly. "East—Hancron. Hancron cleared in '25. And west—that was Lansfeld. He was in '26."

"Three years since the last new clearing was established then," Tau commented. "And in the years before that, how many?"

But Meshler, prodded by their questions, was already reckoning the list, judging by his expression.

"Up to '24 we had one, maybe two, sometimes three new clearings a year. Had four emigrant ships come in '23. Only one since then, and its passengers were mainly techs and their families to settle at the port. The push-out had stopped."

"And no one noticed?" Dane asked.

"If they did, there wasn't any talk about it. Mostly the holding people are self-sufficient and don't come to the port more than once or twice a year—just when they have cargo to ship. There are five-six families to a holding under the signee who puts up the bond. They use self-repair robos for light field work, but robos of that size are no good for first clearing. Since the lathsmer trade has begun, it's been easier. You don't have to crop for the birds, just give them clear living space and put in one or two fields of smes seeds for extra winter food. They like the native insects and a couple of native berry plants and thrive on them. The buyers think that's what gives them the unique flavor and makes them worth more. You can run lathsmers on ground that has been only partly cleared and patrol the field with robos to do the extra feeding. But it takes men and women to pluck for the down export—and that comes in the late spring. Then they take the down, and it's baled at the port."

"So you are getting to be a one-crop world?"

Again Meshler showed uneasiness at Tau's question, as if he might have drifted and never really thought of it before.

"No—well, maybe, yes. They raise lathsmers more and more because they're all that's worth exporting. A one-crop world and no new holdings—" The grim set of his jaw was more pronounced now.

"I'm a ranger. It's never been my concern to do more than patrol, do some mapping and exploring, make the rounds of the border holdings. But, the Council—someone must have realized what was happening!"

"Undoubtedly," Tau agreed. "It remains to be seen if this situation wasn't given impetus to go along on just the road it has been traveling. You saw how those dragons finished off the lathsmers—and they were developed via radiation from the modern lathsmer embryos. Suppose one of those horrors behind the force field, or that antline, were to overrun the perching fields? Or one of those boxes be planted in some outlying district to affect all the birds coming near it—"

"The sooner we get to Cartl's and the com there," said Meshler, "the better!" And the note in his voice matched the set of his jaw.

It was not long before the river formed a vee with its tributary, and Meshler turned the flitter to follow the smaller stream, which was ice-roofed in places. A little later they crossed the first of roughly cleared fields with a roost set up. But there were no lathsmers. And the light skim of snow on the ground was unmarked by tracks.

That first field fed into another, also bare of life. Meshler turned the flitter and made a low run over the clearing.

"I don't understand. These are breeding fields—they are the main roosting sections."

Once more he thumbed the com and sent out his futile call. But the interference, though not as ear-torturingly loud, was still present. He raised again to cruising level and sent the flitter ahead at the highest rate of speed.

Two more fields—and in the last the birds were gathered, black masses of them, milling about. When the shadow of the flitter moved across them, they seemed to go mad with fear, rushing around, some of the smaller ones trampled upon as they wheeled and stretched their ineffectual wings, attempting to fly. The birds made a dark heaving mass, and then the flitter was past.

"I suppose," Tau said, "that such a gathering as that is not natural."

"No," Meshler replied in a single curt monosyllable.

There was a screen on one of those brush-woods and then more fields, which had been more carefully cleared than those for the lathsmers. Here the stubble of some kind of crop pricked through the snow. The river made a long curve and in its bend was the holding.

It was not a house but rather a series of houses and buildings constructed in the form of a square. In the midst of that was a com tower, set well above the outer walls, and bearing halfway up its length the symbol that was Cartl's brand, which would appear on all he sold.

The houses were of stone blocks, but there were roofs of clay, their lower layers, as Dane knew from the inform tapes he had read, baked into tile consistency but over-laying that other earth, which was thickly studded with bulbs. In the spring those would bloom in colorful array, and in the fall their seeds were carefully gathered and ground into a powder that was the planet substitute for off-world coff.

For a world without any native dangers, or so Trewsworld had been designated, Dane thought that the cluster of structures had the appearance of a fort. The houses, their doors all opening on a court within, were linked one to the next with clay walls again planted with bulbs.

A smooth length of ground just outside the gate was the vehicle park. There was a crawler drawn to one side and a smaller scooter, which Dane would have thought too light to travel this rough and roadless country. Meshler set down their flitter there.

The ranger swung out almost before the vibration of the motor was stilled. Cupping his hands about his mouth, he gave a loud hail.

"Ho, the house!"

It would seem that Cartl's holding was as inexplicably empty of life as the first two lathsmer fields had been. Then from out of the wall before them a voice called thinly, "Name yourself!"

Meshler threw back his hood so that his face could be clearly seen.

"Wim Meshler, ranger. You know me."

The voice did not answer. They stood waiting in the cold, Dane holding the brach. Then the heavy door grated open only part way.

"Come, and quickly!"

The urgency in that was enough to make Dane glance over his shoulder. This place had all the marks of a fort under siege. But who—or what—had driven the inhabitants to this extremity? They had seen no living thing except the lathsmers, though the wild fear of those had been a warning that all was not well.

He crowded through the narrow space the gate had opened. Then the man waiting there slammed the portal shut as if he expected death itself to follow in upon their heels and dropped in place a bar to lock it.

The householder was a tall man, wearing a shaggy coat loose about his shoulders as a cloak, the empty sleeves flapping as he moved. He was of a different racial stock than Meshler, being dark of skin, as dark as Rip, his hair a wiry brush, as if encouraged to stand so from his head.

He wore a shirt of lathsmer skin, the inner down left on, though rubbed away here and there by the friction of use, belted in with a wide belt that carried the customary two knives of the holdings men, one at the fore for eating and general use, the ornamentally sheathed one to the back as a sign of adulthood, to be used on the now rare occasions of honor-feud.

His leggings and boots were of furred hide, and with the shaggy coat he seemed as well "feathered" as his laths-mers. But there was something new. In his hand he carried an old-time projectile gun, such a weapon as Dane had seen only in museums on Terra, or which was used on a few primitive worlds where blaster charges were too expensive for importation and the settlers had made their defenses of native materials.

"Meshler!" The man held out his hand, and the ranger laid his beside it, so they clasped each other's elbow in the cus-tomary greeting.

"What's going on?" demanded the ranger, not introducing his greeter.

"Perhaps you can tell us," returned the other as sharply. "Or rather tell Jaycor's widow. He got back here last night just— And all he could tell us was a garbled story about monsters and men. He had been inspecting the far fields when they savaged him."

"Savaged him?" echoed Meshler.

"Right enough. I never saw such wounds! We forted up when we discovered the com was ng—interference! Kaysee took the flitter to the port. But that was before we realized that Angria and the children weren't back! I tried to reach them via com at Vanatar's—no chance. Inditra and Forman took off in the big hopper for there." He spilled it in a rush of speech as if he needed badly to tell someone. Meshler, who had kept the arm grip, now cut into that flow.

"One thing at a time. Vanatar—then he is establishing his holding at last?"

"Yes, they called us by com for a gathering to clear. I had the shakes again, but Angria, Mabla, Carie, and the children and Singi, Refal, Dronir, Lantgar—they all went in the freight flitter. Kaysee had to make the west rounds, Jaycor the east, and Inditra and Forman were setting up the new tooling shed. And what will I tell Carie—Jaycor dead! We set for the noon news from the port day before yesterday. Got only some story about criminals off a trader making trouble and then—slam—interference. We haven't been able to get through since.

"Kaysee got back all right. But Jaycor was late. Then we saw the crawler coming, weaving all over the place, as if it were running on its own. It just about was. Jaycor was in the driver's seat, almost dead. He said something about men and monsters out of the woods—then he was gone!

"We couldn't use the com, so Kaysee said he'd lift in to the port. Inditra and Forman got the hopper to working and went off to Vanatar's to see about the women. With these damned shakes I was no good for anything. Ya, here they come again!"

The tall man began to shudder violently and instantly Tau stepped forward to steady him.

"Vol fever!"

"Not quite," Meshler returned. "It acts like vol, but the reserbiotics won't cure it. They haven't found anything that will yet. Maybe you can do something for him."

The shudders that ran through the overthin body of the settler made him sway back and forth. His head rolled limply back, and he might have fallen to the ground had not the ranger and the medic held him up between them.

"Get him to bed and warm," Tau said. "Reser may not work, but warmth will help."

They half led, half supported him between them to the middle house opposite the gate, and Dane hastened ahead to throw open the door.

That warmth was a remedy used by the settlers was plain, for there was a blazing fire in the wide, deep fireplace, and before it someone had pulled a cot with a tangle of thick blankets. They lowered the man to this, and Tau packed him in a cocoon of coverings, while Meshler went to a pot hanging on a rod that could be swung around to lower it over the flames. He sniffed at the steaming contents and picked up a cup from a nearby table and a long-handled spoon, which he used to transfer some of the contents of the pot into the cup.

"Esam brew," he explained. "It's hot enough to warm up his insides. But he's in for a stiff bout by the looks of it."

Tau braced up the well-covered man and, with Meshler's

aid, got a cupful of liquid down his throat. But when they lowered him again, he seemed to have lapsed into unconsciousness.

Dane set down the brach, who padded over to crouch in the full heat of the fire. The alien gave such a sign of relief and pleasure that Dane wondered how he had been able to stand the cold of most of their wayfaring.

"He is the only one here?" Tau nodded at his patient.

"The way he said it, yes. That's Cartl. He must be half crazy, what with the shakes and knowing he daren't try to reach the women himself. In this cold he would black out if he tried it."

"This Vanatar—so there is another south holding?" Dane asked.

"I knew Vanatar had been talking about coming for about two years now but not that he had really decided. He must have made up his mind in a hurry. Anyway, I've been on detached duty and not on field patrol. Let's see—"

He walked to the left wall, and when Dane followed him, the Terran saw there was a map painted there. Portions with the more or less regular lines of such fields as they had flown over were colored yellow, the uncleared land gray. But to the east was the edge of another set of boundaries, these dotted in as if not permanent.

"Vanatar had this surveyed about five years ago." Meshler indicated the dotted area. "Then he was in two minds about ever taking it up. It lies east and farther south."

Dane examined the gray blot of the wilderness. Where in that was the wood of the force field, the basin? Or was that area on this map at all?

"Vanatar would have no defenses. And a gathering—they would be spread out, working on field barriers all over, women and children watching. If those monsters came at them—" Meshler's half-finished sentences needed no clarification for Dane.

"Take our flitter and try to pick them up?" Tau suggested as he joined them.

"Couldn't take them all at one time," but Meshler was thinking about it.

"This com interference," Dane asked. "how far do you suppose it reaches?"

Meshler shrugged. "Who knows? At least when Kaysee gets to the port, he can bring help."

"There's the LB," Dane said. The LB with Rip and Ali— and that box planted near. What if those for whom it had been intended now knew where to look for it?

But Meshler misunderstood him. "You couldn't fly that. And besides, we have no way of contacting those on board her. At any rate, they will have been taken back to port already."

"There's something else." Tau stood looking intently at the ranger. "What did this Cartl say about criminals off a spaceship? That sounds as if our men may be in worse trouble than when we left. And this mess is of your making, not ours! The sooner the authorities realize that, the better."

Meshler looked exasperated. "I know no more of what is going on at the port than you do. What matters most is right here and now. We've got to see about those people at Vanatar's. Have you tried that detect lately?"

What might lie behind that question Dane did not know, but Tau unhooked the detect from his belt and pressed its button. And the assistant cargo master was close enough to see that the needle swung swiftly, not in a confined space between two of the markings, but halfway around the dial, speeding between north and south points in a whirl, as if it were drawn by two equal forces at once.

"What does that mean?" demanded the ranger.

Tau turned it off, examined the box closely, then started it again, holding it at a different angle. It was to no purpose, for the needle still spun in the same direction as before, still as if it were trying madly to record two different sources of radiation at opposite ends of the compass.

"Can mean only two strong readings," Tau replied.

"Their box and perhaps the LB one!" Dane made a guess. Could the radiation broadcast from the south have stimulated that of the box they had buried to a higher output? If so, how would that affect the LB? But Ali and Rip had had orders to take those left behind in the escape craft into the port. Did it mean they were still there, in the path of possible trouble?

"Could it pull"—Meshler still stood with his hand on the Vanatar section of the wall map—"those things to it?"

"Who knows? Both sources are strong," was the medic's answer.

"There is something." Dane was trying to remember a conversation he had heard on the *Queen*. The com system had been Ya's duty, and all Dane knew were the basic fundamentals of sending and receiving should the need he do so arise. But Ya had been yarning once with Van Ryke, and he had said something about being jammed by a jack ship and what they had done to get a signal through for help. It had been a pulsating counter-jam, which spelled out a crude message by ebb and flow. It was too technical for him to try, but his holding had a com, and someone had to be able not only to operate it but also to know enough to keep it in expert repair.

"What?" Meshler was impatient.

"Something I heard once. Who runs the com here?"

"Cartl mostly. He was a tech at the port when he first came. Got enough planet credit to take up this section. But the com's no good—or—we can see—" He crossed the room swiftly to where a com board almost as complex as that of the *Queen* was built into one corner. The crackle of answer when he opened the beam was not so hard on the ears, but it was steady.

"Still jammed."

Dane looked now to the medic. "How sick is he? Could he come around enough to try something with the com?"

"If this follows the vol fever pattern, he'll be pulling out in about four or five hours. He'll be weak and shaky then, but clear-headed enough. Trouble is I don't know how many bouts he's had, and that makes a difference."

"He can't do anything with the com anyway," Meshler protested. "Don't you think he must have tried earlier?"

"He tried only straight sending," Dane answered. "There's counterinterference by pulsation. And if they have someone with a keen ear on the receiving end at the port—"

"Ya's story about the Erguard!" Tau caught him up. "You might have something at that. But we'll have to wait until he comes around."

Meshler looked from one trader to the other. "You may know what you are talking about. I don't, but I don't see that we have much choice. I am not even sure I can locate Vanatar's holding site."

15. RESCUE ATTEMPT

At last they had real food again. Dane sat at the table where a round of cold lathsmer breast was flanked by a hash of native grains and berries and found it very good indeed after days on one-quarter E-ration tube per meal. Outside, the night closed in, and Tau kept close watch on the semiconscious Cartl, who now and then muttered unintelligibly. There had been no return of those who had gone to Vanatar's, nor of the men who had taken off after them. Nor any sound from the com they had left turned on low, save the clatter that cut them off from help.

"How far are we from the LB?" Dane drank the last of a heated brew and set down his mug to face Meshler squarely.

Twice the ranger had gone to the wall map and studied its lines, ever running his finger along some as if to assure himself they were recorded there. Now he approached the the table.

"Perhaps two hours' flying time at normal speed," he answered. "But why? Your men won't be there. They were to be picked up soon after we left. And they would take the box, too."

"Would they?" questioned Tau. "What about the detect report? I don't think that would register if the box had been taken all the way to the port. What do you have in mind?" he asked of Dane.

"If we had the box and brought it south, I wonder—could it draw the monsters away?" He was fishing, grasping for any hope, no matter how small.

Tau was shaking his head. "Not when we don't know enough about its action. Dane, get me some more of that drink!"

Cartl was moving in the thick wrappings of covers the medic kept piled about him, striving to rid himself of their weight. Dane went to the steaming pot, poured out what was left—half a mug of the aromatic stuff—and brought it to the medic.

"Take it easy now." Tau spoke Basic and supported the settler with an arm about his shoulder. He set the cup to Cartl's mouth, and the other drank off its contents thirstily. Then with Tau's help he sat up, pushing aside the covers. He was no longer shaking, and there was intelligence and purpose back in his dark face.

"How long was I out?" was his demand.

"About three hours," Tau answered. "You must have been in the last stages of this bout."

"Angria—the children—the rest of them?"

He must have read the answer on Tau's face. His hand went to the back-belted knife. "Then—" But he did not finish that foreboding.

"Listen." Dane moved around in front of him. He did not know what Cartl pushed by fear for his family might do, but he felt that it was now or not at all that he must discover whether the settler had the experience to tackle the com problem. "The com's still jammed. But there is a way we might just get a message through and ask for help."

Cartl frowned. He did not look at Dane at all. Instead, he had drawn the honor knife and was running the blade lightly across the ball of his thumb, as if testing its keenness.

"The com's jammed," he repeated absently. Then he turned to Meshler. "You came in a flitter. Let me take that—I'm free of the shakes now."

"For how long?" Tau's demand was so emphatic that it caught Cartl's attention, and he did look to the medic. "You are over this bout, yes. But cold will bring on another. And if you start and then black out, what good will that do you or anyone else? Listen to Thorson here. You may not have heard of what he has to say, but we know that it worked before in a similar situation. You are a com-tech by training, so this should be a way to help your people."

"What is it then?" Now Cartl did give his attention to Dane, but there was an impatience about him, as if he expected to hear nothing of use and resented the trouble of giving judgment.

"I'm no com-tech, and I don't know your technical terms—but this is what a free trader did when his ship was jammed by a jack after his cargo." And he gave the story stripped to bare details.

The knife, which had been moving back and forth in Cartl's fingers when Dane had started, was still.

"Counter-interference in pulse pattern," the settler said. "And what kind of code?"

"Nothing elaborate. Just identification and a call for help."

Cartl returned the honor knife to its sheath. "Yes. And if Kaysee did not get through—" He rose, swaying for a moment but avoiding the hand Tau advanced to steady him. Then he went to the com.

A touch on the switch brought the crackle up to louder waves of sound. Cartl listened intently. His lips moved. He might have been counting.

Then he pulled out a seat and half fell into it, still with that intent, listening look. He reached under the table on which part of the equipment was based and brought out a box of tools. Unscrewing a panel, he switched off the receiver and then went to work, slowly, almost fumblingly at first, and then with more speed and surety. At last he leaned back, his hands resting on the edge of the table, his shoulders drooping a little, as if his labor had exhausted what small strength he had regained.

"That's it. But will it work?" He seemed to be asking that of himself, not of the three behind him.

The brach had been stretched out before the fire, basking in the heat. But now he sat up on his haunches, his forepaws folded over his belly. His head was not turned toward the men in the corner, but there was about the alien an aura of listening that caught Dane's attention, and he watched the brach rather than Cartl, who had set two wires delicately together and was now tapping in a broken rhythm.

Dane crossed to sit on the cot Cartl had lately left.

"What is it?" He had picked up his thermo jacket and spoke into the hood mike.

"There is coming," replied the brach.

"Of that which we must fear?" Dane asked quickly.

"There is fear—but it lies with those who come. And there is hurt also—"

"How near?"

The brach's head swung slowly back and forth, as if his long nose was pointer for a detect.

"Coming fast, but not yet here." That seemed evasive. "There is fear, much, much fear. And all have it."

Dane arose and spoke to the others. "The brach says some are coming. He says they are hurt and afraid."

In spite of that loud mixture of sound from the com, Cartl must have heard. He swung around to face Dane.

"When?"

"The brach says they are coming fast."

Cartl was already on his feet. He did not reach for the shaggy coat he had worn cloakwise earlier, but he did pause to snatch up his weapon. And Meshler was at the door before him, blaster in hand.

They ran for the gate of the fort, Cartl in the lead. The others caught up with him only after he had leaped to a ledge along one of the gate side buildings from which they could see the outer world. The moon was bright, and under it the snow gave back sparks of glitter.

Now they could hear it. There was no wind high enough to hide the steady beat of a flitter engine. Cartl gave a cry of relief and leaned out to hit a button, so that lights flared on, marking a landing space. Meshler half raised an arm as if to turn them off but did not.

There were no running lights on the flier. It came in dark and somehow ominous under the moon. When it set down, they saw that it was larger than the one they had stolen from the basin camp, almost double the size of the one carried by the *Queen*. Round-bellied, it was obviously intended to carry cargo, but now both cabin and cargo hatches sprang open, and a group of figures spilled out so hurriedly onto the field that several stumbled and fell, others stooping to pull them up again, as if those inside were prisoners seeking freedom. Leaving the doors hanging open behind them, they made for the gate. One of the monsters might have been pounding at their heels.

Women—three, four, five, six—children to such a number that they must have been packed shoulder to shoulder inside. And behind them men, two with bandages, helping a third between them who made a stumbling, futile effort to walk.

Cartl threw open the gate and sprang to seize one of the women, one who had two children, one clinging to each hand. As he held her tight, the others crowded around them, crying out in some planet dialect the Terrans could not understand.

But Tau pushed past the women and reached the wounded, with Meshler and Dane only a step or two behind. With their aid he got the three back to the room they had just left.

It was sometime later they heard the full story. These were the women of Cartl's holding and with them three of Vanatar's group, plus the children of both. The wounded consisted of two of Cartl's men and one, who was the worst mauled, of Vanatar's.

They had had little warning. As Cartl had earlier believed, they had been spread out through the fields overseeing clearing robos, the women setting up fires to heat drinks and tending pots of food. Without warning then the nightmare had come. Their accounts of what they had seen and fled from were so varied that Dane deduced the larger part of the attacking force had been made up of more than one type of monster, all of them so alien to what the settlers knew that that very alienness added to the fright and horror.

Some of the work force had rallied quickly enough to trigger the robos in the fields to cover their retreat, and the settlers had broken into several groups. The ones reaching Cartl's had luckily been close enough to the flitter park to fight their way there. But even then, they were not to escape easily, for the monsters were only the first wave of that hideous army. Behind were men, and they had used blasters, though from several accounts, mainly one from the men, the strangers had been both driving on the monsters and defending themselves from them.

A flitter had come to hover over the vehicle park, and a line of monsters had trailed along behind it, almost as if led on a leash. There had been a fight, two of them. And two parked flitters had been smashed past getting into the air, so the settlers' first plan for evacuating this party to Cartl's and then reaching one of the other isolated groups had failed.

"Got them then—" one of the men wearing a bandage down his left arm, strapped to his body, said. "Vanatar had a burner mounted on a crawler and was going to use it on thick brush. Yashty and I reached that. Got that sky-scum in the center. Then Cartl's ship came in so we could take off

151

with the women. I wasn't much use with the arm, and Yashty got a knock on the head, but together we could make one pilot. Asmual had taken a nasty one and was laid out proper. So Thanmore said for us to get out while the air was still clear. They would hold the park with Cartl's men and maybe get that crawler with the burner started so it could make it to the upside. We could still hear them going at that, so we knew some of our people reached it. But even if they hold out a while, they can't do it forever. They have the robos for their main defense and a small burner, but not much else."

"How many of you reached there?" the ranger wanted to know.

The man shook his head. "No telling. We were the largest group, most all women and children. I saw three—three at least get it from those devil things. And two were burned down at the yard before we wiped out that air scum."

"This upside—" Meshler interrupted. "Where is it in relation to the park?"

For a moment the man shut his eyes, as if trying to mentally picture the refuge site. Then he answered, "South a field and then east. It's a big outcrop of rough rock. Vanatar thought it could be made into an extra-secure roost, and he ordered us not to blast it out. It's the best defense they could find there."

"No flitter landing near it?"

The man shook his head. "Only in open ground, and there you'd have to fight off those things. If they haven't overrun the rocks—"

"Could your men get out if a flitter went on hover and we used air rescue belts?" persisted the ranger.

"I don't know."

The technique the ranger suggested was a tricky one. Dane had seen it done at training stations, but the *Queen*'s men had never had to put it into practice. And did the settlers have the proper tackle?

His question was put into words by the other more lightly wounded man.

"You have a rescue flitter here? You'd need the belts and shock lines. And you'll have to hover low. They're using blasters, and if you got down to the right level, one sweep would cut a belt rope."

"We can set the hover on low." Meshler sounded confident, but Dane thought this the wildest suggestion yet. He looked about the room. Tau was busy with the badly wounded man. His place would certainly be here. The three who had come in with the refugee flitter were in no state to go back, and Cartl might have a relapse if he made such an effort at present, which meant that the rescue mission would fall on two of them, Meshler and himself.

The ranger did not ask for volunteers. He put them all, save Tau, to work, improvising the equipment needed. They had finally a bulky belt, plus a double-woven steelion rope and a pulley hoist, which occupied so much of the interior of the flitter that Dane could not see how they could take off more than two, or at the most three, of the refugees at a time. In addition, they had to use the slower flying cargo flitter in order to rig such an installation at all. And even Cartl warned them that any overload of weight on hover might break that down.

But at dawn they took off, Meshler again as pilot, Dane and the brach, who at the last minute added himself to their company, housed in the stripped rear beside the hoist.

"This is bad." Dane tried to urge the alien to stay behind. "We go into much danger."

"Go with you, come with you, always, with you go our own place," the brach stated firmly, as if in Dane alone he had any hope of returning to his mate and family. And knowing how the alien's talents had helped them in the past, Dane could not have him put out bodily.

With the directions of the refugees for a guide, Meshler pushed the flitter at the top speed that the lumbering craft could maintain. Behind them the people of Cartl's holding were preparing for a state of siege, while Cartl himself had gone back to the com, though he seemed to have little faith in the experiment he tried.

There was no storm, but the day was gray, and the sun was a very pallid spot of light, well veiled by clouds. Save for their two blasters, they carried no arms. And Dane tried not to imagine what would happen if the enemy had captured one of the burners and turned it aloft to singe out any attempt at rescue.

When they came in over the fields where Vanatar and his people had been clearing, the ragged scars of the interrupted work were beacon enough. The tangle of the flitter the refugees had brought down lay in a burned-out mess, eclipsing in part two crawlers it had crashed upon.

From that wreckage a lance of blaster fire shot at their own craft. Friend believing them enemy, or enemy trying to blast any rescue attempt? At any rate, that spear of light had come from a hand weapon, lacking power to reach them, though were they to descend, it might make a direct hit—

Meshler brought the flitter around, away from the park. The machine, never meant for fast or limited space maneuvering, needed all his attention at the controls. But it was the brach who gave them their lead.

"Much fear—pain—that way—" He pointed with his nose. Dane interpreted, and Meshler headed in the new direction.

They caught sight of the rocks. They looked from above almost as if they were some artifical erection rather than natural outcropping, though they stood in no pattern, only raised a mass of erosion-pitted stone skyward.

Meshler guided the flitter in closer. Halfway across the roughly cleared field was an overturned crawler. From it pointed the ugly snout of a burner, and where that lay against the soil, there was a long streak of black and smoking soil ribboning from it. Apparently the machine had been overturned with the burner going at full blast, and that had remained on to sear and roast the ground until its heating unit was exhausted.

But it had taken toll before it had been defeated. There were three half-burned carcasses on its back trail, and all of them suggested that in life they had been monstrous. More nightmare things, however, were left to prowl around the rocks, though they did not essay to attack, mainly because scuttling back around the rocky outcrop were three robo clearers, their long, jointed arms with scraper and slasher attachments at ready, threshing the air in a whirl of threat.

Two more robos had suffered. One whipped around in a dizzy circle, two smashed arms trailing behind it, bumping on the ground, half the control box that served it for a head melted away. The other did not move. Apparently its progress circuits had been shorted in some manner, but it whipped and banged the ground in a frenzy.

That these, too, had left their dead was plain from corpses cut and slashed, four of them. But the robos were good only as long as their charges lasted. Even as the flitter went into hover over the stones, two of those keeping sentry go were slowing, and one came to a complete stop, its armored arms raised high, remaining frozen so.

Meshler was fighting the controls of the flitter. As Cartl had warned, the awkward cargo carrier did not have the maneuverability of the craft he was more used to, and he was finding it hard to judge just the right height. Those below must have recognized the craft, for they waved wildly from behind the shadow of stones.

Dane kicked open the hatch and made ready to swing out the belt, but the contrary flitter was bucking, refusing to settle into a steady hover, so that the equipment swung back and forth. Whether the hoist would work, Dane dared not guess. They could only try.

He watched the belt flop loosely down, keeping the rope from tangling. That it had reached its goal he knew when the rope jerked its signal. Now—

He spoke to the brach. "Watch, see if all goes well. I must work this—"

The alien trotted to the hatch and thrust his head out, bracing his feet against one side for hold against the swing of the craft.

"They put fast a man—he has hurts—"

Sending up wounded first. Dane wished they had had the forethought to bring up at least one able-bodied helper on the first try. If the belt did not hold—

He started the hoist, fastened to the motor Cartl and one of the refugees had bolted in hurriedly. The rope went taut, and there was a groan from the motor as the strain began. It took the weight very slowly, too slowly—yet there was nothing he could do except squat here and watch it, make sure that the motor kept on working and the rope fed back evenly.

The wait seemed endless, and then the brach reported. "One is here—he cannot aid himself."

"Come here." Dane made a swift decision. "Watch—if this rope loosens, call!"

He scrambled past the brach, who obediently came to the hoist. The belt spun just below the hatch, the man in it limp and still, having been trussed inside the lift by a patchwork of tatters knotted together. With infinite care Dane got him in, bathed in sweat that was not induced by heat when he laid him on the floor. He tried to take care in loosening those fastenings. Then once more he kicked out the belt and let it fall on the line.

There was no time to examine the first arrival. Meshler did not even look around, his concentration on the controls was such that now he seemed a part of the craft he fought to master.

Once more that jerk on the line, the arrival of another injured man, but this time conscious, able to help himself.

As Dane uncoiled the lashing that held him in the belt, he said, "How many more of you?"

"Ten," the settler replied.

Ten! They could not pack that many in here, not with the hoist taking up so much room. It would mean two trips —and did they have time for that? He threw out the belt again, asked the settler to watch the hoist, and then edged up to Meshler.

"There are twelve. We can't take them all."

Meshler did not turn from the controls as he answered, "We're on borrowed time. We may not be able to make a second trip."

That was obvious. But it was also plain that they could not hope to overload the flitter and get away. So far all they had seen of the enemy were the patrolling monsters outside the robo ring and that one blaster shot from the vehicle park. But that did not mean there had been any retreat.

Suddenly the flitter gave a lurch, just as if they had been jerked ahead on an invisible line. Their hover had been broken. They were moving from the rocks.

"Control beam!" the ranger cried. "It's weak, but with this craft I can't break it."

Control beam! They were being reeled in again, just as they had been in the other flitter. Another crash?

"What the—" He heard the second wounded man in the back cry out, "We're going past the rocks!"

Dane got back to the hatch. Below them dangled the belt. They were already past the rocks, and it was a mercy no one had been in it.

"Look!"

He saw the belt settle as the beam brought them lower and suddenly hook over the up-thrust arm of a robo that had run down. To be so forceably anchored in an instant was the final mishap. In spite of Meshler's skill, the nose of the flitter went sharply up, and they headed tailward to the earth.

16.   BAIT FOR A TRAP

Dane was thrown back by the sudden tilt of the deck. He slammed into the framework of the hoist, his head meeting one of the beams with a sickening crack. Perhaps the padding of the thermo hood saved his life, but from that second he lost all interest in the proceedings.

He awoke with pain filling his head, sending torturing fingers exploring down his neck and shoulders. So did that fill his world that he was only vaguely aware of sound— loud and intermittent—which arose beyond the red haze clouding his vision.

Then he was lifted, and the pain hit with acute force so that he cried out to be left alone. The impatient handling, for he was being pulled along roughly, made it worse, though he did not sink back into full unconsciousness.

He was dropped, rather than laid down, his head a little elevated. Then they did leave him alone. Slowly, blinking, he managed to see a little about him. A mass of wreckage pointed skyward, past his range of sight, for he could not raise his head higher. After slow minutes of capturing memory, he knew that for the flitter, which had apparently struck full on its tail. Scuttling back and forth across his line of sight between him and the stones was a robo waving flailing arms.

"Meshler?" The ranger's name came out as harsh, croaking sound, but the face of the man leaning over him was that of a total stranger. He glanced at Dane casually but made no attempt to examine the Terran's hurts.

"This one's still alive," he reported to someone.

"All the better. If he threshes around a little, it will make it more convincing. What about the others?"

157

"One dead, one still breathing. And the pilot?"

"He's safe enough. With his feet in a tangle, he can flop to impress, too. Push him halfway under the wreck, and it will be all set. Now, give those dust grubbers the message—loud and clear—"

The words seemed to float in and out of Dane's hearing. Some were sharp and clear and made sense. Others were so faint that he could not be sure of them.

"You—up in the rocks!"

That was certainly loud enough to re-echo inside his skull as a frightening din.

"Listen," shouted the same voice again.

Fainter—"We're listening."

"We can make you an offer."

"We're listening—" Almost an echo of the first reply.

"Send a couple of your men out for a talk."

"Send yours here—unarmed," countered the other.

"Give them what they want." Another voice, impatient, cut in. "We haven't much time now. This has fouled up everything."

"We come, no blasters, to that rock—"

"Agreed."

The man who had stood by Dane moved away. As he passed the robo, the machine swung away from him, its personna detection device steering it from attacking a human. Another man came to join him. They stood with their backs to Dane, but he could see them. The haze was clearing more from his vision, and he could watch in a detached way, as if this had no meaning, for the only reality was his pain.

From behind the stones came two men in settlers' shaggy outdoor clothing. They moved warily, and they did not come far, standing well away from the enemy.

"What do you want?" demanded one of them.

"Just out—off-world. We have a spacer we can lift in, but we need time to reach her—and we need transportation—a flitter."

"So? Well, we don't have one," countered the settler. "And we can't make one out of stones—"

"Give us a truce," returned the other. "We call off the beasts, send them in another direction. There's a broadcaster to the north they'll drift to if we switch off ours. And we'll send in a com for help. Whoever comes will see this wreck and set down by it. We'll take over. Oh, not with blasters—with tanglers. Then once we're out of here, you're free. All we need is that flitter. We would have taken this one if it hadn't fouled that blasted robo. You stay where you are, quiet and peaceful. Don't try any tricks until we get the flitter. Then we'll go—"

The settler turned his head to his companion. Dane saw their lips move but could not hear even a whisper of speech from where he lay.

"What about them?" The settler pointed to the wreck and Dane.

"They stay here until the flitter comes. After that you can have them. And to show you we mean what we say, we'll call off the beasts, hold them back. If you agree, that is."

"We'll talk it over—" The settlers' spokesmen withdrew, not turning their backs on the enemy, but edging along until they disappeared behind boulders large enough to give them cover.

The others tramped back, though they took no precautions against fire from the stones. Something beside the fury of pain moved in Dane. He understood the terms of the truce, but it did not mean much to him personally. Only a dim sense of alarm awakened. It was clear that the settlers did not trust these men, but would they agree? And if they did—

Bait! The explanation rang in Dane's mind as if it were an alarm to awaken him to what this might mean in terms of his own survival. The fragments of talk he had heard on his first regaining consciousness made sense. He—the others who survived the crash—were to be left here as bait!

Another flitter might set down to give them aid. If the beasts had been called off and there was no sign of enemy activity, that could work. But suppose that the men among the stones made no move to warn off the newcomers—the trap could spring shut at once.

But would the strangers, once they had their means of transport, merely withdraw? Dane fought the steady throb of pain in his head and tried to think more clearly. Let the settlers believe that, and they were fools.

On the other hand, they were not well armed, and the robos were running down. The one that had been whirling back and forth behind the wreck of the flitter was just coming to a stop. It gave one or two more flails of its arms; then froze pointing straight out, as if to push away an enemy it could no longer attack.

So without blasters, with their robos run down, they would be easy meat for the monsters. And the refugees might just be desperate enough to take a chance at a bargain, believing that they could not be any worse off and that it might save them. Dane's need to warn was giving him a kind of strength now. He tried to move, at least one hand. It came up slowly until he could see it hanging limply on his wrist, as if it were not his but another's. Now he turned his will on his fingers. They were numb, without feeling, but they did move as he ordered.

Being able to wave a hand was not what he needed now, but more, much more. He concentrated upon sitting up. But when he raised his head from whatever slight support it lay upon, the world whirled in a spin about him, and he nearly blacked out again.

So he lay quiet, using what strength he had to move his other hand, one foot a little, then the other. At least he did not seem to have any broken bones so far. And the numbness was wearing out of the hand. Perhaps the knock on the head and a general drastic bouncing about was all the damage he had suffered.

"Do you think they'll agree—"

Dane subsided at the sound of that voice, behind and quite close.

"What choice have they? After those robos short out, the beasts will swarm at them. They're not that stupid. Let them take a little longer to argue about it, and then give them the ultimatum—now or never!"

"How long do you think we'll have to wait for a flitter?"

"Well, that one bunch got away, and these came prepared for a pickup. Manifestly, they knew what they had to do. So somewhere the alarm has already gone out. And Dextise got a message from the port. The free traders seem to have done enough talking to impress Largos and the Patrol commandant."

"I thought Spuman was handling that so well—"

"He had it all tied up until this last shipment blew it. Grotler couldn't have made more mistakes if he were deliberately trying to foul jets. A good thing he didn't finish the voyage alive. Dextise would have taken him apart bone and muscle and fed the remains to one of his pets. This may well have finished the whole operation. It will if Spuman can't use the Trosti cover. One man—just one man—plays it stupid, and we lose three years of work! And maybe the big cover into the bargain."

"Grotler must have been sick. He died, didn't he, during takeoff?"

"Let us hope that part of the story is straight. If he was helped out of this universe, then matters may be even worse than they seem. No, Dextise has the right of it now—cut our losses here, get off-world, and let these bird-tenders argue it out with the big ones. Dextise will turn on the agitators to send the monsters crazy and spread 'em out. The settlers will be so busy jetting around to pull their own people out of the jaws of this and that from Dextise's pens that we'll have time to cover our trail a little. You'll learn there comes a time when you sometimes have to write off an operation."

"You think this might blow the whole Trosti deal?"

"Who knows what the Patrol is going to find when it noses around? We could maybe have covered up Grotler and the free trader if that ranger and the traders hadn't come snooping around, and if they hadn't broken the force field and let the big ones out. Nothing to do after that but try to control them. And we couldn't because of some counter call to the north."

"Grotler's?"

"What else? The trader didn't bring it in. Last we heard from Spuman, they admitted they landed it in an LB somewhere in the wilderness and planted it where they thought it would be safe until some tech saw it. By the fourteen horns of Mablan, this thing fell apart right there and then! We tried to head them off, and what happens? We run into this—"

"Dextise said wipe 'em out. Let the rangers think the beasts did it."

"I know, I know. Then what happens? Some of them get away! So then we have to wait around to make sure these won't talk if help comes—and we lose a flitter. If you want to take a crawler back when you know some one of the beasts can open one of those like an E-ration tube and have you out as if you were rations—"

"So now we hope for another flitter."

"Can you think of a better way? Eilik has killed the inter-ference. He's sending an SOS through on the port reading, purposely making it weak. Between her and the port, there're four or five big holdings. Any one of them might respond—that's settler custom. So we get a flitter, and then we turn the agitator on high, and with their robos not functioning, Dextise will still get his wish—nothing left alive to talk."

Though there were still missing pieces in the ugly pat-tern, it made sense for Dane, more than anything had since he had seen the dead man in his bunk. Just as he had feared, these strangers had no intention of keeping their part of the bargain. How could he get a warning to the men at the stones?

"You—out there—" The refugees were the first to call this time.

Dane tried to make his body obey his will. If he could only call out! But when he tried it, the best he produced was a harsh croaking. One of the strangers, passing, looked down searchingly and then deliberately kicked at Dane's outstretched legs, the jar of that blow running like flame up his body until he thought he was going to black out. When he recovered a little, he could see the strangers and the settlers again facing each other.

"We agree. You call off the things, and we'll let you have the flitter—if it comes."

"It'll come," the stranger returned. "We're beaming a dis-tress call north. You make no warn-off signal. We're holding the beasts back. You do a warn-off, and we let them go. And they'll get these first—" He gestured over his shoulder to the wreck and perhaps the other survivors Dane could not see. Was the brach among them?

Again he had half forgotten the alien. Since the strangers had not mentioned the creature from Xecho, it might be that the brach had been crushed somewhere in the flitter, a nasty end for the unusual comrade of this painful adventure. Dane's hood was crumpled under his head, and when he inched around a little, trying to see if he could reach the mike of the interpreter, a sharp point dug into his neck, so he flinched away. It felt as if the com had been crushed and was now reduced to broken metal bits. So much for that. He could not summon the brach even if the alien was alive and had escaped injury.

162

But the Terran had other things to think of when the men came back from the stones and halted to stand over him. Both of them were of Terran or Terran colonial stock as far as he could judge. They wore thermo jackets not unlike his own, and their heads were hooded, though they had pushed the masking visors up and back. One of them squatted now on his heels, though he did not put out a hand to touch Dane.

"You heard that." It was not a question but a statement. "All right, you don't fire rockets now and throw this off course. If you do, we let our pets back there loose, and who do you think they'll relish first?"

Dane did not reply, and the man seemed satisfied that he had thrown fear into a hopeless and helpless captive. He added, "We ought to take care of you anyway. You blasted traders got us into this mess. If it hadn't been for you—"

"Come on." His companion dropped a hand on his shoulder. "No use in planeting in on him with all that. Fact is— Grotler did it, not them. Grotler and what we could never have foreseen. He's finished anyhow."

They both vanished out of Dane's range of sight, and he was left to stare at the wreck, the still robo, and the stones, with the words "finished anyhow" remaining in his mind. But something in him responded to that as if it were a lash laid unexpectedly on his back.

So they though that he was finished, that all that was left for him was to lie here, acting as bait in their trap and then falling to one of their monsters! If he could only see what lay behind him— What they had said earlier—that Meshler was all right, only they had put a tangler on his legs and shoved him under the wreck to play the roll of another victim—

There was no brach to free them this time. So, whatever could be done, Dane would have to do for himself. Once more, slowly, and with infinite care, he tried to move arms and legs. This time they responded better. It was almost as if that kick had removed some block. Also the pain in his head was now stabilized as an ache, fierce to be sure, but it no longer made the world whirl about him.

He tried to judge time by the look of the sky. The clouds of the morning had held. He had no idea how long before real dark. But surely the jacks would rig some kind of light to draw the help they thought would come. They would not waste their bait in darkness. How much light?

Dane listened as intently as he could. He could hear the clanking of the last two robo defenders of the stones and —just barely—a murmur of voices from some distance— not loud enough to distinguish any words.

Water—Spirit of Space—how he wanted water! It had been a nameless need at first, but now that he thought of it, his thirst was enough to swallow up his judgment if he allowed it to. Dane had always thought of himself as being tough—free traders were noted for their ability to take about the worst any planet could offer and, if not survive, manage to make a battle of it. There were techniques taught on Terra—survival methods that did not come out of kits, or supplies, but had to lie inside a man himself. Dane had not been very good at them. He doubted whether he could be better now. But when there was only one road left, that was the way a man must go.

He went to work following the methods that had been so drilled into him, though his response then had often been the despair of the instructors. Mind over body—only he was no esper—

Thirst—he was thirsty. He felt as if he could lie in a pool of water and absorb it sponge fashion through every pore. Water! For a moment he allowed himself to think of water, or the dryness of his mouth, the ash-coated emptiness of his throat. Then he deliberately applied the right technique— or what his instructors half the galaxy away sitting comfortably before a class of aspiring spacemen declared was the right technique.

Water—he wanted it, so it followed that he must get it. To do that, he had to move. And to move, he must again be able to command his body. But he was hampered now by the fact that if he showed too much life, his captors might see to it that he was quiet again.

Dane's arms lay by his sides, but his palms were against the ground. Stealthily, he exerted pressure. He lifted a little and discovered that more of his weakness had ebbed, and he could raise himself.

Could he counterfeit delirium? And dare the enemy treat him too roughly in sight of the stones? They had made a bargain, even if they did not expect to keep it. Suppose he tried to move and they attacked him. Those watching might believe they dared expect no better treatment. That kick had been delivered in passing and when to their sight he might have been unconscious. So—

Dane put pressure on one side. It also depended on where he was going to go. If he tried to roll toward the stones, they would stop him, but if he turned to the wreck? There was nothing left to do but try.

With what strength he could summon, he pushed, rolled on his side, and lay quiet, while once more pain and dizziness washed over him. But now he could see the wreck fully, and not far away lay another body sprawled out face down. It was the badly wounded man they had taken on board, and plainly he was dead. A little farther on was Meshler.

The ranger stared at Dane, and now he wriggled vainly. From the chest down, with both arms and legs out of sight, he lay under what had once been the hatch door, while leaning over him at a threatening angle was one of the hoist beams.

"This one's moving!" Dane could not see the speaker, but the man must be close behind him.

"Water—" Dane thought it time to play his role. "Water—"

His voice was still harsh, hardly above a whisper, but he managed to articulate better this time.

"Wants a drink, he does."

"Well, give him one. Don't let them see us off beam now, or they might get ideas—"

Dane felt warm. He had been right in assessing the position. Then a grab at his shoulder brought him on his back, and he had time only to see the nozzle end of a space cup coming abruptly down to spray its blessed moisture into his mouth. The first spray was so delivered that he choked, and some of it spilled out of his mouth to run across his chin, into the folds of his hood. Then the nozzle was between his teeth, and he sucked avidly.

"Drag him over here," came the order as the nozzle was pulled from his toothhold with the same brutal disregard for his pain as when it had been first inserted. "He's too near the stones. Someone might have a bright idea about trying to get to him when it gets dark."

Hands caught in his armpits, lifted him a little, and then dragged him back along the ground. He could only endure that jolting with what small store of energy he had left and hold on to consciousness as if that were a weapon someone was trying to twist out of his grasp.

When they let go, he thumped back against a surface that supported his head and shoulders much higher than before. And the squirming Meshler was almost within touching distance.

"Excellent—" Dane half opened his eyes. He was not playing a role now, he was living it. He could see blurrily a man come to stand before him.

Man? No, this was an alien like the one who had been in the camp below the ledge, if not the same one. He spoke Basic. At least that one word was in the Basic of the star lanes, but the accent was pronounced.

"Yes, well done, Yuljo. He is now a sight to wring the hearts of any rescue party. Doubtless he dragged himself hither to try to free his trapped comrade and then collapsed. Very well staged—since your breed on these frontier worlds is too much occupied with the thought that they owe a duty to one another when disaster strikes. If this weakness did not grip them, we could not hope to lay our little trap at all."

He raised his head, encased in no thermo hood but rather in a tightly fitting helmet from the back of which projected an antenna—not a space helmet but perhaps an off-world com device. Now he looked to the north. Did they expect help so soon, Dane wondered? As far as he could judge, they were hours away from any northern holding, and there would not be another party come from Cartl's.

"It would be well to set the lamps. There is no storm, but we face a dark night."

Indeed, the gloom had increased since Dane had last noted it. But situated as he was now, he could view more of the scene. Of the other man they had rescued before the crash, he could see nothing. Perhaps he lay on the other side of the wreck. Meshler was still, though his face was turned to the Terran, and he gave Dane a sharp glance now and then.

Their captors were working with two camp diffuse lamps, making adjustments to their shades to throw a maximum of light—one on the wreck and the two men there, the other to mark out a landing site for the craft they confidently expected to entice in.

Why did they not use the control beam again, wondered Dane, and then found an answer for himself. They had tried that, and it had ended with a wreck. They did not want that to happen again.

Having set the stage with care, the alien gave a last-minute inspection. Two of his men took cover in the shadow of the wreck, using pieces of the flitter to give them protection from the sky. And each was armed with a tangler.

The alien came once more to stand before Dane and the ranger.

"Hope or pray to whatever gods you own," he said, "that you do not have long to wait. We are holding off the beasts, but we do not have equipment here of any great strength, and how long we can so hold—who knows? This is a game of chance and one in which you and those fools behind the stones there have the most to lose. There goes their last robo—and how long will two blasters and a brace of stunners hold against what prowls out there—once it is loosed?"

He waved to the expanse of half-cleared land, and Dane saw that nightmare and horror did prowl there. Most of it was beyond his power of description but enough allied to perils he knew to make him understand just how black the future was—more so than a moonless night, for there were no stars to light it.

17. PURSUIT TO THE RAT NEST

"We must depend," the alien continued, "upon that weakness of your breed, that, seeing one of their kind in distress, they must straightway come to his assistance, emotion outweighing caution. We are giving them a piteous sight indeed."

Dane thought he detected black humor in that, as if the

alien considered this a source of laughter for *his* breed. But was he taking into consideration that this was a too well-set stage—that anyone with an ordinary amount of suspicion answering a distress call would be wary of a so well-lighted and arranged scene of disaster? Supposing Cartl's counter impulse had broken through the earlier interference and— But Dane must not build upon hope, only accept what lay starkly before him now. If those who answered the call for help, always supposing they did, were not suspicious—

The alien was walking away.

"They can do it," Meshler croaked, as if his throat were dry and the words rasped painfully from it. "From the air this must look all right. And if we try to warn them—"

"We have no hope anyway," Dane answered. "I heard them talking." Dane could not believe Meshler ever thought the jacks would keep their word.

The diffuse lamps were on, set in such a way as to suggest that at least one able-bodied man had escaped the crash of the flitter and was endeavoring to provide a guide for a rescue craft. The skill in placing that limited illumination was such that both Dane and Meshler were fully revealed. Any move the Terran might make would be instantly visible to those in ambush.

But the men waiting there had tanglers, not blasters. Did that mean that the enemy was running low on charges for the deadly weapons and were saving what they had? And how many of the monsters remained?

With the robos frozen when those were turned loose— Resolutely Dane tried to cut that picture out of his imagination and think about the immediate future and what might be done for the two of them in the here and now. Only he could see nothing at all!

He would like more water. Water—no, do not think of water, which was now as far from him as the *Queen* herself. The *Queen*, the LB—what had happened to his own star-going world? Apparently the box was still in the place where it had been buried, or else it would not be acting as a draw on the monsters. So its radiation must be able to pass the safeguards Stotz had set on it, acting as a contact beam.

Dane was so deep in his thoughts, thoughts that could lead nowhere, that he was not at first aware of the cold metal sliding under one of his hands as it rested on the ground, but the persistent nudging of that touch drew his attention at last.

The Terran dared not look down. Not only was he afraid that might awaken his dizziness, but also, if what he guessed was in progress, through some wild stroke of luck, he must not allow those in ambush to suspect. Stealthily he moved his hand, raising it a little. Instantly the object that had been nudging him pushed between palm and earth, first a barrel, and then the butt, worked carefully around so that his fingers could close on it.

A stunner! The brach! The alien from Xecho must be hidden by the wreck and was so supplying him with a weapon. It was far inferior to a blaster, to be sure, but better than the tanglers in ambush, though he could not be sure how much of a charge was left in it.

Another nudge against his hand. Dane touched the barrel of a second arm. But this one was gripped tight, held so for only a moment, and then withdrawn, as if the brach only wanted him to know that there was a second weapon. Dane remembered how the creature had faced him on the *Queen* —he knew how to use a stunner. If Dane could only communicate—suggest that the alien work around the flitter and use the stunner on the two in ambush. But that was impossible.

He tried to feel for the paws that must hold the second weapon, but there was nothing. He might have thought it a fever dream, except that he still had the first stunner.

The dark was drawing in fast, and the diffuse lamps were bright in the dusk. It was what prowled out there that fretted the nerves. A stunner—what good would a single stunner be when the breakthrough came? Don't think of that now. Could he reach either of the men in ambush? Dane edged his head around, kept his eyes half closed, yet was able to see a little from beneath drooping lids. Suppose the rescue craft came—might he take out at least one of the jacks before they could use their tanglers? And would Dane dare —or would he be answered by blaster fire from the shadows where the rest of the enemy had gone?

How many jacks were there? The alien, who appeared to be in command, at least six others—more probably. It was a wild, crazy, fruitless plan, but it was all Dane had to cling to.

The keen edge of expectation can last only so long, and waiting is a fret that saws it very dull. Dane had known such waits before action in the past, but never had he been so helpless before.

The night was not silent. There were the ominous sounds made by the things that prowled about, kept in check by their masters. Somehow, hearing them was worse than seeing them.

But at last, through those growls, snarls, hissing, there came another sound—the steady beat of a flitter engine. Dane, stretching his head farther up and back, tried to sight nose lights, but the craft must be coming from the north, and he faced south.

"Coming—" Meshler rasped. The ranger tried to heave his body out from under the wreckage, which held him tight. "Can't you do something—warn them?"

"Don't you think I would if I could?" Dane retorted. But there was no sense in moving or revealing his weapon until he could make that really count.

The sound died away, to Dane's surprise, and then he was sure the pilot was wary, was going to run a survey of the scene before landing. Would suspicion keep him aloft? With a sinking of spirit Dane could not deny, he thought he had guessed right, for the muted drone of the engine grew fainter and vanished. Would that be a signal for the enemy to loose the monsters, since their trap had been rejected?

But apparently the jack leader had patience and confidence in both his scheme and in his knowledge of human motivation, for those in ambush did not move. And his confidence was vindicated when once more that hum came through the night, now from the south, where the flitter had vanished.

This time Dane could see the nose lights, green as the glowing eyes of a night hunter. The machine dipped very low, pointing almost directly at Meshler and him. Then the craft went into descend, the drone of the motor louder. Dane looked at the one jack he could see from his position. The man was tense. He held the tangler so that the adhesive stream, which would congeal instantly on contact with flesh, would spurt into the small portion of ground anyone must cross to reach Dane and Meshler.

The Terran could not see beyond the lights. He did not doubt, however, that the rest of the enemy company was on the move, drawing in to be ready for attack when the flitter touched ground, but not until they were sure, he supposed, that all were out of the craft. Otherwise the pilot could lift, leaving them empty-handed.

What followed was almost as if his thoughts had been broadcast, picked up by esper. The forehatch opened before the tripoint of the landing gear touched the ground, and a figure leaped free from the flitter. He landed on his feet and ran, not straight for the two by the wreck, but in an evasion pattern, as if he knew of the ambush. At the same time, Dane dared to move. He rolled to one side, taking the jack by surprise—or perhaps the other was astounded that the flitter, having discharged only one, gave an upward bounce to go on hover over the wreck.

Dane fired, using his own body to partly screen his action. And though he had no time for a good aim, the near arm of the man with the tangler fell to his side. He lost his grip on the weapon and skidded forward trying to regain it. The Terran had not knocked out the enemy, but he had rendered him a one-armed warrior for several hours at least. The runner reached Meshler, sliding over the last bit of space between them, squirming around to fire his own stunner. And he had better aim. Its beam struck the man still flopping after the lost tangler in the head, dropping him instantly.

Fluid lines spun by a tangler in the hands of the other ambusher spun out through the air. He fired on a net setting, and those fine threads would automatically seek the nearest human flesh to which they had been conditioned. Unfortunately for him, in order to reach the newcomer who had hunkered down beside Meshler, he had to edge a little into the open. And both Dane and the man from the flitter fired at the first inches of arm and shoulder he was forced to reveal for that shot.

The tangler still spun, its sticky output fountaining now straight up as it fell from his hand. A moment later those strands found a target, the man himself, spreading avidly about his head and shoulders.

"How bad is it?" Rip's voice broke through Dane's wonder at the shot, which might have been aimed by fortune herself.

"A knock on the head. But they're ready to send their monsters at us. And there're the settlers in the stones—"

"I think they will have other things to occupy them," Shannon answered. "As for worrying about their monsters—" He pulled from the front of his thermo jacket one-handedly, keeping the stunner on ready in the other, a box. Pushing in a plunger at its top, he said, "Where are the monsters?"

"That direction the last I saw—" Dane leaned away from the wreckage. The world still had a tendency toward a side-slip, but he fought that off.

"Good enough." Rip got to his feet before Dane could protest against so exposing himself. He drew back his arm for such a throw as sped a sleep-gas bomb and sent the box flying out into the dark. Dane felt a strange crawling sensation along his skin, and the pain behind his eyes awoke to a new agony.

"Sonics," Rip explained briefly. "That is tuned to the ant-line's frequency. Let's hope it picks up everything else they've turned loose from their misbegotten menagerie."

A moment later he dropped between Dane and the ranger as a tracer of blaster fire cut along the wreckage at what had been the level of his head and shoulders. The sear breath of that fire was a wave over all three of them. But, while Dane tried not to expect that another beam would crisp them, a second lance did not flash. Instead, there was confusion out in the night—cries, more tracers of fire, none however aimed in their direction.

"That does it," Dane heard Rip say close to his ear as they sprawled shoulder to shoulder on the ground. "They'll have plenty to think about beside us—"

"What—?" Rip did not let him finish the question. He was quick with an answer, as if he believed reassurance would be a good restorative.

"We didn't come straight in, you know. Landed some Patrolmen, two rangers, and a couple of port guards by grav-jump belts. We then provided the distraction while they went into position behind. That's their force moving in now. The sonics will set the monsters on the run away from here—"

"That box from the *Queen*—they said it had drawn the monsters north—" Dane cut in.

"Just as well. They can be picked off then as they trail in that direction. Now, what about you?" Rip levered away the piece of wreckage that had been left to cover Meshler. Once his tangle bonds were revealed, it was easy enough to dissolve them. The ranger, groaning as he swung cramped and stiffened arms and legs, crawled out.

The flitter, which had hovered over them, was setting down again, not too far away. But this time there was no bounce to send it aloft, instead, the hatch opened, and a couple more men dropped out.

"Captain Jellico!" Dane recognized the first. The second wore the uniform of the Patrol, but it was modified on the collar by the winged, star-studded staff of the medic service, and the stranger carried an aid kit in one hand.

"What have you been doing to and for yourself, Thorson?" The captain went down on one knee and drew Dane up a little.

"Watch out, sir!" Dane caught at Jellico's sleeve and tried to pull him farther down. "They've blasters."

"And they've plenty of use for them elsewhere," the captain returned. "Let's have a look at you—"

In spite of Dane's protests, he found himself lying under the competent hands of the medic, who reported a little later, as he gave Dane a restorative shot, "Skull intact, but you took a bad knock. And this"—he threw away a handful of metal scraps—"gave you some cuts. Now, sniff this."

He broke an ampul under Dane's nose. A sharp scent stung the Terran's nostrils, clearing his head, and the pain became only a faraway suggestion of ache. He lay resting, the medic having gone to the stones and whomever there might need him. But though the captain vanished during the time his hurts were being assessed, Rip was still near.

"Where did the captain come from?"

"Long story," Shannon answered. "Too long to tell now. But Cartl got his message through. And we were already on the move south. We heard enough of the second call from here to know it was probably a trap. So the Old Man was prepared."

"Cartl said the news came through that the crew was in prison, charged with sabotage."

"It began that way, until there were too many things to add up for even the thick-headed port police. Then they began to listen to us, a lot of questions were asked, and there were several answers to each one. The Patrol took a couple of local councilors into custody and had them probed. That was a serious step to take—might have lost the officers in charge their jackets and space rights if their suspicions hadn't been verified.

"But it isn't only a cleanup here—the thing's bigger than just Trewsworld. And if the Patrol hadn't been already nosing around, perhaps we wouldn't have had our hearing so promptly. It all goes back to the Trosti foundations—"

"Thorson"—he was interrupted by Jellico as the captain came into the light—"how many men did you see here?"

"Six, seven, most of Terran or settler stock, I think. But their leader was an alien. They needed a flitter badly—had to get back to their camp. They were planning a withdrawal off-world—"

But the captain no longer seemed to be listening to him. Jellico gave a pull of his thermo hood, drawing it forward a little, and Dane caught sight of a com set in its side, much like the arrangement he himself had used to talk to the brach.

The brach! Why was it he kept forgetting the alien who had twice saved their lives—three times if you could count the breaking of the force field? It was almost as if something deliberately willed memory to sink to the back of his mind.

Now from behind the wreck trotted the creature from Xecho, walking on three legs. The fourth was folded up against his belly holding the second stunner. From the flitter dropped another brach, running with speed to meet her mate. They touched noses and then swung about, shoulder to shoulder, to face the Terrans.

Captain Jellico swung up his wrist, peeling back his glove to lay bare another mike, resembling the personna coms used by explorers.

"Finnerstan, some kind of a small airborne craft just took off—heading south. The brachs report it has one of the jacks on board. My guess, judging by what they are able to scan, is that it is the jack leader. And he must be heading for their command post. Intercept—"

There was no reply except a confirm click from the wrist mike. Dane sat up and waited apprehensively for his head to punish him. But, thanks to the medic, he was able to move, if weak. Rip got to his feet and reached down a long arm. And, pulling on it for support, Dane made it, too.

"Heading for the basin—"

"Basin? What basin?" Jellico demanded.

Dane muddled through the story of the force field prison, of the jack headquarters beyond. Jellico pushed his hood a little back and pulled at his lower lip. His expression—which was not really an expression but a stillness of feature—was one Dane knew of old to be the prelude to action.

"They had a flitter before," he said, "that was brought down by the settlers. That was what they set this trap for, to get another flitter. They had to get back—they have a spacer there, and they wanted to take off."

Captain Jellico came to sudden life. "Finnerstan, they have a ship waiting for planet lift—at a base to the south. Have you anything to patrol that way?"

The reply came as a squeak. Jellico frowned, holding the com close to his ear.

"The sonic," Rip half whispered to Dane. "It interferes. And I don't think they will be able to broadcast back to the port with that on. If they shut it off—"

"Exactly!" But whether Jellico meant that in answer to Shannon or to what the squeak conveyed, Dane was not sure.

"Meshler should know the location of the basin," Dane offered. But looking around, he could not see the ranger.

"We have detects. They just won't work around the sonics. Come on!"

Dane and Rip, the two brachs trotting ahead, as if they had had some forewarning, fell in behind Jellico moving to the flitter. But with his hand already on the hatch, the captain turned to look at Dane.

"You're on sick call, Thorson."

Dane shook his head and then wished that he hadn't, as a warning thrust of pain suggested such gestures were not for him at present.

"I've been there—" It was a thin plea; Meshler would be the better guide. But somehow he wanted to see this through to the end. And when three men in Patrol uniforms and one of the spaceport policemen came running, he was vindicated, for when the ranger was asked for, the report was that he had gone back to the park to see if any vehicles could be brought to transport the wounded.

In the end they were a mixed expedition. The two brachs had squeezed far to the back of the flitter, crouched down side by side, as if fully determined to stay where they were, daring anyone to pull them out. For the rest there were three Patrolmen, their leader, Finnerstan, who came up just before they slammed the hatch, the spaceport policeman, two rangers, plus Jellico, Rip, and Dane.

It was rather a tight fit, and the captain himself had the pilot's seat, Finnerstan beside him, the rest of them packed in the back. This was no cargo flitter, rather a troop carrier from the port, so that they at least had seats—hard though those were—and did not have to squat.

Dane was behind Jellico, and as the captain lifted the flitter into the air, he asked without turning his head, "Which direction?"

"South and west—the best I can do, sir."

Finnerstan turned a little around to give him a measuring stare. "There is nothing there. We combed that district for months—"

"They are in a basin," Dane returned, "and have rigged a distort over it. From above you can't see anything—"

"A distort!" Finnerstan sounded incredulous. "But on such a scale as that—it is impossible!"

"From what I have heard and seen"—Captain Jellico's tone was cold—"these Trosti people have proved a lot of impossible things possible. I imagine once they are all run to earth, there are going to be a lot of preconceived scientific ideas turned inside out, back to fore. A distort, eh? How did you find it then?"

"We followed a crawler track."

"That gives us something—if we have daylight when we get near enough. But we have to make time. I don't like the idea of something flying south. Pilot arrives with a warning, and they'll lift off-world. Then—" He spoke to Finnerstan. "You may have finished their scheme here and now, but all you will have left are the pieces they have left behind. I can imagine they will leave precious few of those. What they can't lift with them, they'll destroy. And that's the last thing we must let them do. Once we're out of range of that sonic, you'd better code in a call. See if you can get help from the port. The *Queen* isn't armed well enough to take on a ship in space. What about your cutter?"

"She can try," but Finnerstan did not sound too certain. And Dane thought that with the curious devices these jacks appeared to have for their equipment, he could well understand the other's apprehension.

If Finnerstan thought dark thoughts, they did not prevent him from experimenting with the flitter's com until it was clear. Then he sent out a call, repeating it several times in code numbers, until a click of acknowledgement came. He dropped the mike back in its holder and said, "The cutter will space and go on patrol. Maybe she'll be in time— They are widening their radar, so anything taking off from this continent will register."

"Time," Jellico echoed. "Well, we have no way of buying time unless we can anchor them some way. But there is no use making plans until we are sure we have something concrete on which to base them."

18.   SPOILS TO THE VICTORS

"What *is* going on?" Dane turned to Rip, wedged in beside him.

"What isn't?" returned the other ambiguously, but then he explained. "We don't know it all yet, but the Trosti foundations, here and apparently on other worlds, too, have been engaged in double work. The surface stuff is all that has always been accredited to them, what their reputation is founded upon. But underneath that, well, the Patrol has evidence now that they are the power behind at least four planetary governments in widely separated sections and that they have been building up an undercover net of control—"

"Who are *they?*" Dane interrupted. "Trosti is gone—or is he?"

"That's just one of the mysteries, though there are two explanations for that. One is that he is still very much among the living and the brain behind this all, or else the brain who has selected the brains, for the conspiracy is a composite effort, and not only of one species either. The other suggestion is that Trosti was never anything but a front for a devious and diverse organization who used clever publicity to promote him as a romantic figure to center attention.

"Anyway the Trosti foundations are a form of shadow government by now, though apparently the Patrol has been suspicious for some time. But it was only when they made the slipup on the *Queen* that enough of their plans were revealed here to give the law a loose end."

"I know they have an outlaw experimental station here with the retrogressed monsters," Dane said. "But is that all?"

"It might have begun so. Then they discovered something else."

"The rock!"

"Ore," corrected Rip, "and a very special kind. It is useful in esper work—a conductor for low-level telepathy, able to step up that and other esper talents to a remarkable degree. It exists on several planets, but it was not recognized until they built the retrogress machines and probably is one of those chance discoveries that happen as a side effect of a main experiment when the scientist in charge is intrigued enough to follow it up. There is reason to believe that most of this experimentation had been going on right here. They wanted Trewsworld. The holdings were a threat to any open work. Hence the monsters, which were developed and released gradually to drive the settlers out."

"The Patrol knew this and didn't act?"

"The Patrol suspected. Then we came in. The Trosti man at the port wanted us silenced. But short of killing us off, he couldn't do that. The captain appealed to the Board of Trade representative, and since the Patrol was in on that appeal, they had their opening. Though the Trosti had the Council here very much tied to them, they did not have any control over the Patrol. Where the Council tried to make things hot for us, once the captain had made his statement, the whole thing blew up in their faces, like a gas ball.

"And, as a gas ball, it was a knockout for them. They probably knew it, thought they could buy some time to ship their important records off-world by loosing the monsters—"

"We did that—or rather the brach did." Dane cut in with his story of the force field barrier and the fact he had over-heard the jacks' talk of the monsters being drawn north by the other box. "But those prospectors"—he remembered suddenly—"if they weren't Trosti men, how did they— Or," he ended, "did they know about the rock?"

"Our guess is that they had some kind of new detect, and it registered enough of the unusual radiation from the ore to make them believe they had found something. They took samples, but it must have been from a vein the Trosti crowd had mapped, and they were killed, the rock taken. It was a quick job and another botched one. I would say that lately the Trosti has not been too well served by its people. That elaborate affair of shipping the box on the *Queen*—"

"Yes, and if they already had the ore and such boxes here, why take the chance of shipping another in?"

"One of the minor mysteries. Perhaps, this—our box—was from another one of their labs, sent in for checking. And it must have been from a place where there was need for extra cover, so that it had to be sent so. It was their bad luck that we had the brachs and the embryos in the cargo and that their man died. If he had made it undetected to port, all he would have had to do was rip off the mask and disappear. But it was a chance, and there must have been some pressing need to take it. When the Patrol backtracks we may know why someday—unless this will all be top security."

"Trosti—hard to believe that Trosti—"

"That statement will be echoed on a good many different worlds." One of the Patrolmen broke into their exchange. "Trouble is that the discoveries they did make for the benefit of the worlds on which they set up are generally so beneficial that we will have to have direct proof that those were only a cover or we can't go against public opinion—plus the fact that they will summon top legal talent and be able to fight a delaying action in every court we take them to. We are hoping that this, now being the most open of their secrets, will give us evidence—records, tapes, enough to smash this foundation, with clues to uncover leads to others."

"If we get there in time," Dane pointed out. "They could ship out the most important material and destroy the rest."

His head was starting to ache again. Perhaps the remedies of the Patrol medic were not as long lasting as he hoped. He could understand the need to conquer time, which was driving the captain, all of them on board. Also, they had no idea of what defenses beside the distort were in the basin. There was the control beam that had negated the power of the other flitters and brought them down at the will of the enemy. And such could be used to deliberately crash a ship. The jacks need only have one of those in order, and their pursuers would lose before any fight began.

There were plenty of other weapons to snap them out of the sky at the press of a button. Unfortunately, memory presented too many in all their savage details to Dane. But once more it might have been that his thoughts were as plain to his companions as if his forehead was a transparent visa-screen.

"They can't use a control beam if they are readying for a takeoff," Rip observed thoughtfully. "That would interfere with a blast, set them off course from the first fire-down—"

"Even if they don't use that, I can name about five other defenses," Dane returned bleakly. He leaned his aching head back against the wall and closed his eyes.

"Have a suck." Something was thrust into his hand, and he glanced down to see he was holding a tube of E ration; the heat cap had been twisted off so that a small thread of steam arose. For the first time Dane realized he was very hungry. He raised it to his mouth, his hand shaking a little, and squeezed the paste, warm enough to spread a welcome heat as it passed downward, into his mouth. It was a very long time, he thought, since that meal at Cartl's holding, even longer since he had eaten regular food at established intervals.

But the E ration, though it gave a man nothing to chew on and lacked much flavor, did banish hunger. And this time he was not limited to a quarter of a tube. He had a whole one to himself, while those about him were eating, too.

"The brachs?" For once memory worked as he swallowed the first mouthful.

"Have theirs." Rip nodded toward the rear of the cabin. The light was limited, but Dane could see an E tube protruding from each horned snout.

"What about them?" he asked a little later as he squeezed the last drop from the tube and rolled it into a tight ball.

"The kits are at the lab, being given Veep Treatment," Rip answered. "But the female insisted upon coming with us. There has been a lot of excitement over them. If the brachs are degenerate intelligent life, then Xecho is going to have a problem. And it would seem that is true. It will probably be obligatory to do what can be done to return them to their proper intelligence—upsets a lot of history and will be quite a headache to all concerned."

"Are they esper at all?" Dane wondered.

"We don't know just what they are—yet. The lab has dropped all other experiments and is concentrating on them. It may be, since the principle of the retrogress machine is linked with the esper-inducing ore, that anything with a slight degree of such power has that power heightened. That's another headache—"

"Ha—" That was the Patrol officer. He held out his wrist, and on it was a detect, not unlike the one Tau had carried, except more compact and much smaller. "Radiation of the right type, two degrees west—"

"Right!" Jellico made the correction in their course. "How far?"

"Less than two units. It is leaking through a shield."

Dane saw the captain's head give a little jerk. A moment later Jellico reported, "The brachs say there's a ground transport of some kind, two of them, moving under us."

"Could it be they are still pulling in men?" suggested Finnerstan.

"Pulling in men," Dane thought, and yet just this flitter load proposed to go up against what might be a thoroughly warned, armed, and well-defended base. Yet, looking about him from face to face, he saw no concern. They might have been making a routine flight. Though he was no longer hungry, the pain in his head remained a steady throb, and he felt very tired. How long had it been since he had had normal sleep? He tried to recall events for the past days, days that now seemed to stretch to months. Jellico was not noted for taking reckless risks unless the situation was such he had no other choice. No free trader did and kept a ship for long. But apparently the captain was determined on this attack.

"Only one unit ahead now." Finnerstan did not look up from the detect.

"Radar nil on anything airborne," Jellico replied. "Mixed report from the ground, a lot of interference."

Dane turned his head and tried to stretch to the point where he could look down from the cabin window. But it was physically impossible to see the ground from where he sat, even if it had been day instead of the dark of very early morning.

"No contact beam." Jellico might be reporting to them or only thinking aloud.

"I'm getting something new—maybe your distort." Finnerstan glanced back at Dane.

"All right, Thorson, what's down there?" Jellico demanded, and Dane pulled his thoughts together. This was the time when he must justify his inclusion in his company.

"Spacer landing to the south." He closed his eyes, picturing in his mind what he had seen during their quick sortie into the basin. "Then there are three bubble huts in a cluster about seven field lengths north—beyond those two long structures half buried in the earth, earth walls, turfed roofs —vehicle park by the bubbles. That's it."

"They will be expecting their men back in a captured flitter perhaps," Jellico said. "And that would come in without hesitation. So, we try to do it that way."

And maybe meet blaster fire dead center if there was some recognition code, Dane knew. He wished vainly that he had some kind of protective shell into which he could withdraw during the next few minutes. But the Patrol officer made no objection to Jellico's wild plan.

"Look there!" Finnerstan was against the cabin window on his side, staring down. But for the men behind him there was no chance to see what had caught his attention.

"Down." Jellico's hands were busy on the controls. "That must be the distort. Now, I'm going in on hover—"

Dane saw movement about him. The Patrolman by the exit hatch had his hands ready on the lock there. And the flitter began its descent, straight down, using the slow speed of the hover.

There was an odd light outside the windows, light that brightened suddenly, as if it had been turned from low to high. Perhaps it had been the passing of a blanketing of diffuse lamps by the distort. But now they were apparently descending into a camp brightly aglow to aid activity.

"Now!" Finnerstan rather than the captain gave that order, only a second before the bump told them they touched earth.

The Patrolman wrenched open the hatch, made the practiced roll out and down, his neighbor following him in trained proficiency. The spaceport policeman and rangers followed with less agility.

Finnerstan himself had already disappeared through the front door. And now, before Rip and Dane pulled themselves out, the brachs flowed away with a speed surprising in their stocky bodies.

Rip jumped. Dane was the last to disembark, his reflexes slowed, but he held a stunner in one hand. Jellico had vanished and was probably on the other side of the flitter.

As his boots met the ground, the thump of contact transmitted to his aching head, Dane looked about. It was light, but by some lucky chance they had landed some distance from the scene of the activity. The spacer still stood, its nose pointed to the stars. Both its cargo hatches were wide open, and cranes were at work loading. There was a line of robo carriers speeding from the two earth-walled buildings, each bearing boxes and canisters, but their burdens were small. They were taking only lighter, easily stowed things, Dane judged with the eye of one only too used to handling shipments. The rest they would probably destroy.

There was one crawler pulled up with two cages on board, covered. But that stood by, and no one was there. The ramp leading to the crew and passenger quarters was still on the ground and—

Dane was startled. That ramp was under guard. Two men in crew uniforms stood at its top, just within the open hatch. They were both armed with blasters, and they were looking steadily down the ramp. Now that he studied the scene, he could see in addition a similar guard on duty by the two cargo-hold openings, both eyeing the load the robos stacked to be taken on board.

So far no one on the field seemed to notice the landing of the flitter and the disembarking of her passengers, but there was a knot of men nearer to the ship. They just stood there, their hands hanging empty by their sides, staring at the guarded ramp and the cargo holds.

"No room." Dane heard Finnerstan's low-voiced comment. "The Veeps are planning to leave their underlings behind. I wonder if they will agree—"

"They're disarmed, sir," one of his men reported.

There was an addition to the clanking of the robo carriers, to the general hum of the loading. It did not come from the group of men bitterly watching the preparations for withdrawal but from a distance. Then two more crawlers plowed on into the bright light around the ship.

The first carried only three men, each with a pack or box he supported against his body, as if to shield it from the jerks and jostling caused by transportation across very rough terrain. The second had one large, shrouded box amidships.

As the crawlers passed the waiting men, there was a confused shouting, a slight surge forward as if they would have rushed those transports. Then a lance of blaster fire cut across the ground, laying down a smoking reminder to stay where they were. As they had moved forward, so now they stumbled back, away from that searing bar.

The crawlers did not halt, nor did their occupants so much as glance at the rejected. Instead, they moved steadily forward until they stopped by the ramp and the one cargo hatch. The lines of robos had come to a halt. Most of them were shut down and stood in a compact group, which grotesquely mimicked that of the frustrated men. Only two were still activated, and they went to work transferring the crate on the second carrier, working with exaggerated care that suggested their burden was of great importance. As they were making fast the lines for it to be lifted into the hold, the men on the other carrier started up the ramp, bearing their burdens with the same visible need for safety.

"About time for takeoff," Jellico said. "We have to move now—"

But someone else had the same idea. While they had remained in the shadow of the flitter, watching the scene and trying to estimate their best chance, the brachs had sped into action. Now they saw the male rear on his hind quarters, holding a stunner in his forepaws. He was at the foot of the ramp, and his ray beamed up in a back and forth sweep intended to take out the two guards.

They must have been so intent on watching their human opponents that they did not sight the alien until too late. The last man carrying a package stumbled, fell back, sliding limply down the length of the ramp, so that the brach had to leap out of the way. While that victim had deflected some of the stunner, he had not taken all the ray. From suddenly deadened hands above fell one of the blasters. The other guard, momentarily startled, aimed not at the brach but at those he knew were enemies, the group to be left behind, his fire cutting into them so that those not directly crisped by its beam scattered, some screaming.

Now those on guard in the still open hatch took up the fire, before crumpling under stunners used by the brach, while the second guard, still firing, fell at last, rolling in turn down the ramp, his blaster yet emitting a beam, whirling its deadly lance right and left as it bumped by him and then fell to the ground.

"This is it!" The Patrolmen, followed by the others from the port, went into action, speeding for the ship. For takeoff, the ramp must be in, the hatch closed. Now one of the brachs darted out of hiding to reach for the blaster still discharging its fire power along the ground. But he or she did not reach it. There was a lance of fire from the hatch, poorly aimed, for the alien was not hit, merely went to ground again.

However, the force of Trewsworld law closed in about the spacer, centering their aim on the open hatches, picking off anything trying to close that.

Dane stumbled along in the wake of the captain and Shannon. He found it hard going, and they left him well behind. But neither of the free traders were heading for the battle of the hatches. Instead, their goal was the third carrier, the one with the two cages on it. Rip reached it first, scrambled into the driver's seat, and was warming her for a start when the captain hurled himself in on the other side, half standing, half crouching, prepared to defend their capture. And defend it he did as several of the rejected, who had survived the burn-off, tried to rush the Terrans.

Jellico got two of them. Dane picked off the last, numbing his leg with a stunner. Rip set the carrier on high and was bringing it around, aiming it. Now Dane understood what he was trying to do. The weight of the carrier, if it was rammed up on the end of the ramp, would anchor the ship to the ground. There would be no takeoff because the safety factors of the spacer would not permit.

There was still firing by the spacer, and Jellico was alert, watching for any sign of life at the hatch, any chance of Rip's being picked up out of the driver's seat. The assistant astrogator had the blunt nose of their vehicle pointed straight on target now.

Dane saw Rip's arm raise and fall, a stunner held by the barrel so its butt could be used as a hammer. He was breaking the controls. And with those gone, no one could turn the heavy machine from its course.

Rip leaped out one side, Jellico the other, and the crawler clanked steadily on. There was a grating, a crushing sound loud even through the shouts, the crackle of blaster fire. The carrier's nose arose over the edge of the ramp, and the machine hung there, its treads cutting more and more deeply into the ground as it strove to push ahead and could not. But the anchor the free traders had devised would hold, though the ultimate taking of those in the ship might prove to be delayed. If help came from the port, they might be able to use gas bombs.

With the ship so anchored, part of the besieging party rounded up what was left of the men who had been scattered in the blaster attack. But Dane trailed Jellico and Finnerstan on an inspection of the base. Much of what had been there had been purposefully destroyed. One of the earth-embedded structures was caved in by an implosion bomb, and the others all gave the appearance of hasty plundering. A well-equipped com station had been left without destruction, and one of the port policemen slid into the seat there, sought the channel, and beamed a call for assistance.

"Trouble is," commented Finnerstan, "if they are really fanatical about secrecy, they will destroy what they have in the ship." He looked at the spacer as if he would have cheerfully broken it open as one cracks an eggshell to get at the yolk. "By the time we get help, they will have disposed of everything we want."

"Parley?" suggested Jellico.

"Only give them more time to get rid of everything suspicious. If this was a local operation, a true jack raid, we might make a deal. But this is too big. They'll have information on board that must have threads out to perhaps half a dozen other worlds, perhaps some we don't suspect at all. What they carry is more important than the prisoners."

"What," Dane asked, "about those?" He pointed through the door of the com room to the men who had been rounded up. "They won't have any reason to support the ship people, and perhaps they can give you some idea of what *is* on board and whether they would readily destroy it."

Dane's suggestion might already have been in the Patrol officer's mind, for Finnerstan was already moving to such an interrogation. Most of the sullen men were uncooperative, but the fifth he questioned gave them the lead they needed. Though the others captured were mainly guards and workmen below the level of third-grade tech, expendable, the fifth man brought in was a reeling, half-conscious captive who had been rescued a few inches from having his life crushed out of him by the crawler on the ramp, the last one boarding who had been brought down by the brach's assault.

He was certainly of higher rank than the others. In fact, as the guards brought him past those other prisoners, two of them lunged for him, cursing. He was cowering, obviously badly shaken, when he stood before Finnerstan.

The combination of the stun attack, his close brush with death under the crawler, and the anger of his followers broke him. The Patrol officer learned what he wanted. Under his direction they dragged out of the wreckage in the base a tube by which they lobbed gas bombs into the opened hatches. Those broke on contact, spreading the sleep-compelling atmosphere. Masked guards from the flitter went on board to gather up prisoners, leave them wrapped by tanglers, then proceeded to put in safety all that had been about to be transported off-world.

It was three days later in Trewsport that the crew of the *Queen* were finally united for the first time since the LB had taken off. The settlers' government had been badly shaken. There was an interim Patrol command in control, and specialists from off-world had been summoned to examine the Trosti labs and the material taken from the ship.

Dane sat nursing a mug of coffee. His headache had gone at long last, leaving him feeling curiously light. He had slept away some twenty planet hours and was now able to summon alert attention to what Captain Jellico said.

"—so as soon as they clean her out, she's to be put up to auction as contraband taken in the midst of an unlawful act. There's no one here planetside who wants a spacer or would know what to do with her if they had her. We will probably be the only bidders, as the Patrol is not going to go to the trouble of flying her to another world just to sell her. I have it on Finnerstan's word that if we put in a time bid, she's ours!"

"We have a ship—a good ship!" Stotz protested with the firmness of one not to be influenced.

"We have a good ship tied up by a mail contract," Jellico returned. "We have the mail fees, yes, but they are small. And if we can build up a fund as a starter when the contract is finished—"

It was a big step, expanding from the *Solar Queen* to a two-ship holding. Very few free traders had ever done it.

"We do not have to keep her long," the captain continued. "I do not even say deep space with her. Use her in this system only. Trewsworld is an Ag planet. But if she can grow more crops—short-term crops—than just the lathsmers, she would be sooner ready for regular stellar trade. Now look here." He flashed a picture from a reader onto the wall. "This is the Trewsworld system. Those captured charts show that while there is some of that ore—they're calling it esperite—on this planet, there is much more on Riginni, the next planet out. And that can be dome-mined but can't be terraformed. So, miners have to eat, and they have to ship back ore to here for galactic transshipments. There's a two-way trade for you—steady, growing as the dome mines grow. And considering that we had a good hand in breaking up this Trosti mess, we can get the franchise. Profit all along."

"And a crew?" Steen Wilcox asked that.

Jellico ran a fingertip down his burn scar. "Mail run is easy—"

"*Easy*," thought Dane, but did not say it aloud.

"We stagger our own men for a while. You lift her the first time, Steen, with Kamil for your engineer, Weekes as jet man. We hire on a local for steward. And, Thorson, since Van Ryke is on his way in to join us on the *Queen*, you can take cargo master. Next time around, Shannon can take astrogator—we change back and forth. We'll be short-handed, but an inner-system run is easy, and you can get by with robos and a limited crew. Is it agreed?"

Dane looked from one face to the next. He could see the advantages Jellico had mentioned. That there would be difficulties the captain had not mentioned, he could well guess. But when his turn came, he added his assent to the others'.

They would bid on the spacer, begin a solar run from Trewsworld to her neighbor, spread their crew thin over two ships and hope for the best, be ready to face the worst as free traders so often had to. And what was the worst going to be next time? No use in allowing his imagination the chance to paint a dismal picture, Dane decided. The *Queen* had survived much in the past. Her new sister ship would have to learn to do the same.

The World's Best
Award-Winning Science Fiction
Comes from Ace

029363	Armageddon 2419 A.D.	Nowlan	75c
061770	The Big Show	Laumer	75c
067017	The Black Star Passes	Campbell	75c
371005	Interplanetary Hunter	Barnes	95c
516559	Falling Astronauts	Malzberg	75c
531517	The Mightiest Machine	Campbell	95c
535708	The Missionaries	Compton	75c
623801	The Omega Point	Zebrowski	75c
642405	Other Days, Other Eyes	Shaw	95c
734384	Roller Coaster World	Bulmer	75c
951467	You're All Alone	Leiber	95c

Available wherever paperbacks are sold or use this coupon.

EDGAR RICE
BURROUGHS

Just 75c each

033218	At the Earth's Core
046326	Back to the Stone Age
056523	Beyond the Farthest Star
218024	Eternal Savages
469973	Land of Terror
470120	Land of Hidden Men
514026	The Mad King
535880	Monster Men
645101	Outlaw of Torn
658526	Pellucidar
659425	People That Time Forgot
751321	Savage Pellucidar
797928	Tanar of Pellucidar
901918	The Wizard of Venus